**Robert Jackson** is a prolific author of military and aviation history, having become a full-time writer in 1969. As an active serviceman in the Royal Air Force Volunteer Reserve he flew a wide range of aircraft, ranging from jets to gliders.

PRAISE FOR ROBERT JACKSON:

'The descriptions of weaponry . . . are authentically detailed.' – *Publishers Weekly*

'Takes you to the heart of the action.' – Tom Kasey, best-selling author of *Cold Kill.*

*Also by Robert Jackson*

When Freedom Calls

Battle Flight: A Yeoman Series Omnibus

The Romanov Mission

The Last Secret

Wind of Death

# THE INTRUDERS

## The Secret Squadron: Volume One

## ROBERT JACKSON

ENDEAVOURINK

AN ENDEAVOUR INK PAPERBACK

First published by Severn House Publishers Ltd
in 1997

This paperback edition published in 2017
by Endeavour Ink
Endeavour Ink is an imprint of Endeavour Press Ltd
Endeavour Press, 85-87 Borough High Street,
London, SE1 1NH

ISBN 978-1-911445-41-8

Typeset by Palimpsest Book Production Ltd, Falkirk, Stirlingshire

Printed and bound in Great Britain by
Clays Ltd, St Ives plc

www.endeavourpress.com

# Table of Contents

# Chapter One

Dieter Wenninger had approached southeast England by this route many times, droning sedately towards London's Croydon Airport at the controls of a Junkers 52 passenger transport of Lufthansa, Germany's civil airline, in the days before the War. He was completely familiar with the outline of the Thames estuary, the patterns of Kent's rolling countryside, and the smoke-shrouded sprawl of Britain's capital itself, away in the distance. But this was the first time he had seen any of it from close on 39,000 feet.

From this altitude, under a dome of indigo sky, his vision was limited only by the thin veil of haze that shrouded the far horizon. Away to the right, the prominence of East Anglia formed a great curve that bit deeply into the North Sea, while out of the other side of the cockpit the south coast of England swept away towards the Isle of Wight, past Eastbourne and Brighton and the other holiday resorts he had so often visited in happier times.

Ahead of him, and more than seven miles below, he made out the thin, irregular chalk-mark of white that was the cliffs of Dover. Outside the cockpit, although this was the first week of July, the air temperature was 70 degrees below zero, the oxygen-starved air so thin that no human being could survive in such an environment for more than a few seconds. It reminded Wenninger constantly of how thin and fragile the Earth's atmospheric shield really was, and how easily it might be stripped away. But in the pressurised, heated cockpit of the Junkers Ju 86P he and his observer were safe from the hostile elements beyond the thin metal walls, and at this height they were safe from interception. Wenninger knew that no British fighters could reach him, not even the Spitfires that were being supplied to the RAF's front-line air defence squadrons in growing numbers. He did not mind that vapour trails were streaming from the Junkers' twin Jumo 207A radial engines, trails which, on this clear summer's morning, would be visible from the ground; nothing could touch him. He exhilarated in the feeling of security.

The aircraft he was flying was a prototype, a high-altitude reconnaissance version of the standard Ju 86, which had been one of the first modern bombers to enter service with the newly formed *Luftwaffe* in the mid-1930s. The Ju 86P had only flown for the first time in February 1940, and this particular one – one of only three in existence, so far – had been assigned to the Reconnaissance Group of the *Oberkommando der Luftwaffe*, the German Air Force High Command, for operational trials.

On this morning of 4 July 1940, Wenninger's mission was to photograph the Thames estuary, where a merchant convoy was reported to be building up, and then take shots of the cluster of RAF Fighter Command airfields in Kent – Biggin Hill, Hornchurch, West Malling, Lympne, Hawkinge, Manston – that lay like a defensive shield to the south and east of London. The sun was still rising, so that any aircraft parked on them, camouflaged or not, would cast a distinctive shadow that would enable the photo interpreters to identify them accurately. The low-angle sun would also show up any mounds of earth that might betray the position of anti-aircraft installations, or underground fuel and ammunition dumps. Pieced together, the photographic evidence would provide vital intelligence for the *Luftwaffe* bomber crews who would soon be pounding the RAF's fighter airfields to bits.

Although he was not privileged to any inside knowledge, Wenninger was certain that an invasion of England was being planned. He knew that the German Navy was moving destroyers and fast torpedo boats into the newly captured French Channel ports, and with his own eyes he had seen long barges being moved by rail towards the Channel coast. He was astute enough to know, however, that before an invasion could be attempted, the *Luftwaffe* must win mastery of the sky over southern England; then it could turn its full fury on the warships of the Royal Navy, which – with air cover – was more than capable of tearing an invasion force to shreds.

Without air cover, it would be a different story. First, RAF Fighter Command must be utterly smashed, and that meant the destruction of its forward airfields.

The Junkers was over the Thames estuary now, and the observer was lying prone in the nose position, his finger on the trigger that operated the cameras. He needed no instructions from Wenninger; all he required was for the pilot to hold the aircraft steady. Peering down through the glazed panel a few inches in front of his face, he could make out a cluster of dots on the water far below. There was no doubt about it: a convoy was getting ready to sail.

In the equipment bay, the cameras clicked away steadily. The observer knew that when the images were enlarged they would still be crystal clear, thanks to the superb Zeiss optics with which the cameras were fitted. At length, he reported that he was finished.

Wenninger flew steadily westwards until London was beneath his wings, then made a detour north, briefly crossing the Thames so that the observer could photograph Hornchurch. He found no difficulty in locating the airfield, which he had secretly photographed from his civil airliner in the months before the war; Biggin Hill and West Malling were also easy to identify. Wenninger turned back towards the Channel and his last three targets, the airfields near the Channel coast.

Several thousand feet below him, a lone Spitfire clawed for altitude, alerted to the presence of the intruder by the RDF stations on the coast. The pilot had been tracking the Junkers for several minutes, guided by the ground controller at Biggin Hill. He could see it clearly now and he armed his eight machine guns, turning the knurled knob on top of the control column from 'safe' to 'fire'. He switched on his reflector sight and turned the rheostat to its maximum power so that the deflection circle and the dot in the middle glowed brightly; he needed the extra brightness, for the morning sun was a fierce glare in the cockpit. His altimeter showed 35,000 feet and the Spitfire, according to the rate of climb indicator, was wallowing upwards at a mere 400 feet per minute.

Even though this was one of the latest Mk II Spitfires, and its Merlin engine was roaring smoothly, it was making little headway in the rarified air. The pilot could feel his stomach distending painfully, for the cockpit was unpressurised, and to make matters worse the cockpit canopy and windscreen were freezing over. He could still see the intruder, but only just, through a narrow three-inch patch that was free of ice.

He was gulping down oxygen, gasping for breath, belching as he did so. His seat harness and Mae West lifejacket felt as though they were crushing his pressure-expanded body. The ice-free hole at the bottom of the windscreen was only an inch in diameter now, and he knew that he was going to have to abandon the chase.

In a final desperate gesture, he pointed the Spitfire's nose in the general direction of the enemy aircraft and pressed the gun button. Nothing happened. The guns were frozen solid.

Gasping out a string of curses, the pilot swung the aircraft away and dived towards the warmer layers of air below. The Junkers 86P flew serenely on, still dragging its contrails behind it as it headed out over the Channel, its two-man crew completely unaware that another aircraft had come within a couple of thousand feet of them.

Several hours later, the convoy that had been photographed by the Junkers as it assembled in the Thames estuary was off the south coast, churning its way through the Channel. The convoy's official designation was OA178 and it was America-bound, its fourteen merchantmen laden with cargoes that varied from worsted yarn to cutlery forged in the steel mills of Sheffield. War or not, Britain's commercial trade had to continue.

More importantly for Britain's chances of survival, the ships would return with arms; arms for the divisions which, in a pitifully weakened state after the disasters in France that had ended with the embarkation of the British Expeditionary Force from Dunkirk, were trying desperately to fortify the English coast to meet the threat of an invasion which Britain's leaders knew must soon come.

The French campaign had cost the British Army nearly 700 tanks of all types. It had also cost 880 field guns, 310 heavier artillery pieces, 500 anti-aircraft guns, 650 anti-tank guns, 6,400 anti-tank rifles (the latter no real loss, as they were utterly useless against the *Panzers*) and 11,000 machine-guns, together with thousands of tons of ammunition. In the whole of the United Kingdom, whether on issue to units or in store, there were only 54 anti-tank guns, barely enough to equip one division, and 2,300 Bren light machine guns, enough for one division and one brigade. There were 420 field guns, most of them obsolete, with 200 rounds per gun, and 153 medium and heavy guns with 150 rounds each.

Five of the available infantry divisions were responsible for guarding the English coastline from the Wash to Selsey Bill. All were under-strength and short of weapons of every calibre, especially heavy weapons. The five divisions should have had a combined total of 360 artillery pieces; instead, they had only 101 between them, mostly dating from 1918. Perhaps most serious of all, the five divisions could muster only twelve 2-pdr anti-tank guns between them; their total establishment, on paper, was 240.

There was a glimmer of hope in the gloom. Although the United States President, Franklin D. Roosevelt, had proclaimed the neutrality of the United States upon the outbreak of the war in Europe, and had placed an embargo on the shipment of arms to any of the belligerents, this embargo had been ingeniously side-stepped in November 1939, when what became known as the 'Cash and Carry' scheme came into force. Under this scheme, belligerents could buy arms from non-governmental armaments companies, as long as they paid in dollars and provided their own shipping to transport the goods across the Atlantic. In practice, the scheme – which became law by a narrow Congressional vote on 4 November 1939 – was of benefit only to the Allies.

Within a matter of days, a British purchasing commission was established in the United States and was buying up material on a massive scale. Since the United States was forbidden to sell arms directly to a belligerent government, the United States Steel Export Company was nominated to handle the deal. Deliveries were initially slow, and with the urgency that followed the German victories in France and the Low Countries Britain's Prime Minister, Winston Churchill, made a plea to President Roosevelt for the release of reserve arms stocks that were surplus to the requirements of the US War Department.

The call for action went out from the White House, and within forty-eight hours a list of surplus equipment was being prepared. During the first ten days of June 1940, after loading at arsenals all over the country, freight trains converged on Gravesend Bay, New York, and it was from there that the first laden cargo ship, the SS *Eastern Prince*, sailed for England on 13 June. In her holds she carried 48 crated 75-mm field guns, 28 million rounds of small arms ammunition, 15,000 machine guns and 12,000 rifles. A dozen more ships, with similar cargoes, set sail individually before the end of the month.

No matter that the weapons were old, or that they had

been packed in grease for the past twenty years. When the grease was boiled off the elderly P-14 rifles and 1917-pattern Colt 45 pistols, the majority would work. And among the shipments were some excellent close-quarter weapons: .45-calibre Thompson sub-machine guns, the 'Tommy guns' of the pre-war gangster movies.

Convoy OA178, when it returned, would double the amount of arms shipped from the United States to Britain at one stroke. General Sir Edmund Ironside, commanding the Home Defence Forces, was staking much on the hope that the convoy would be back in its home ports before the enemy invasion developed.

But the convoy would not return. It would not even reach the Atlantic. It would not get past Portland, thanks to a high-flying Ju 86 and the photographs it had delivered to *Luftwaffe* Intelligence on the previous day.

On a cluster of airfields around Lannion, on the coast of Brittany, ninety Junkers Ju 87 Stuka dive-bombers were already running up their engines. They belonged to *Stuka-Geschwader* 2, and they had been hastily deployed to Lannion from their main base at Falaise so that they would be better placed to attack Convoy OA178 before it made its exit from the Channel into the Atlantic. Two waves – sixty aircraft in all – were to attack the ships; the remaining wave would dive-bomb shipping and installations in Portland Harbour.

The Stukas began taking off just before noon, led by the *Geschwader* commander, Major Oskar Dinort. Burdened by the weight of the single 250-kg bomb slung under each aircraft's fuselage, the Stukas climbed laboriously to 12,000 feet and set a course towards the English coast. The sun was fierce in the long, glasshouse cockpits, and pilots and gunners soon found themselves sweating; the gunners took care to wipe the sweat from their eyes, for at any moment RAF fighters might come tumbling down upon the formation.

But no RAF fighters appeared, and the dive-bombers droned steadily on, each formation flying in two waves of fifteen aircraft, stepped up in echelon to starboard. Before long the English coastline rose out of the summer haze, and the crews could make out clusters of bright dots, like pinheads, above certain parts of it. They were looking at the balloon barrage, positioned above the key ports. The Stukas assigned to the Portland attack would have to fly through that, but air reconnaissance had revealed the position of every balloon, and the German pilots had planned their approach carefully so that their speeding aircraft would pass through clear lanes between the balloon cables.

The Isle of Wight was off to starboard, and Portland Bill was dead ahead, with Weymouth nestling beyond it. But Dinort no longer had eyes for the coast. Almost under the Stuka's nose was the British convoy, the big freighters ploughing along like fat ducks, trailing their herringbone wakes. He could see no sign of any escorting warships.

Dinort issued a few curt attack instructions to the other

aircraft, then picked his target. As the freighter slid past his port wingtip, the pilot quickly carried out his cockpit checks. Radiator flap closed; supercharger off. Then he stood the Ju 87 on its wingtip and continued rolling, keeping the target in sight all the while through the cockpit canopy. He continued rolling until the aircraft was on its back, then pulled back the stick until the Stuka was diving vertically, the freighter visible through the blur of the propeller blades. Dinort adjusted the attack angle to 70 degrees; with the dive brakes fully open the Ju 87 went downhill at only 150 m.p.h., a speed that made for very accurate bombing.

The freighter was centred squarely in his sight. At 3,500 feet he pressed the release button on the control column and the aircraft shuddered as the bomb dropped away. He broke away in a climbing turn, the force of gravity pushing him and his gunner down in their seats, momentarily blurring their vision. Gaining altitude, he turned back towards the convoy to watch the rest of the attack, and to observe the result of his own.

The freighter was already shrouded in smoke, on fire and listing heavily. She was the *Britsum*, 5,255 tons, and she was the first to die. In the next few minutes she was followed by three more, victims of the other Stukas' bombs: the *Dallas City*, 4,952 tons, the *Kolga* of 3,526 tons, and the 1,796-ton *Deucalion*. Six more ships were damaged.

From their vantage point in Portland Harbour, the crew of the auxiliary anti-aircraft ship *Foylebank* had watched, appalled, as the distant Stukas wheeled and dived like sinister birds of prey over the luckless convoy on the horizon; had seen the geysers of water kicked up by the near misses, the red flashes of direct hits, the mushrooms of smoke rising from stricken ships.

The *Foylebank*, built by Harland and Wolff ten years earlier and requisitioned for war service by the Royal Navy, was a big ship of 5,582 tons, as big as a cruiser and practically its equal, although by no means as fast; her twin-shaft diesel engines gave her a top speed of only twelve knots, but that was enough to keep up with the merchant convoys she was dedicated to escort. She was well armed, too, with eight 4-in, eight 2-pdr and four 20-mm anti-aircraft guns. Had she been out there with the convoy, she might have made all the difference; but her orders were to remain in Portland to add to the strength of the harbour's AA defences.

As Major Dinort's dive-bombers sped away over the Channel, their work of destruction completed, the sirens wailed over Portland and the *Foylebank's* crew leaped to their action stations. Seconds later, the third wave of Stukas came plummeting down on the harbour, holding their dives steady through the anti-aircraft bursts that began to fill the sky, releasing their bombs and jinking away seawards between the barrage balloon cables.

The attack was over very quickly, and by the time it ended the *Foylebank* was ablaze and sinking, ripped apart by three bombs. Sixty of her crew were dead. The little tug *Silverdial* was also sunk, and three large freighters in the harbour damaged. One Stuka, a victim of the anti-aircraft barrage, fell from the sky in a glare of exploding fuel tanks and plunged into the sea. The other twenty-nine got away. Not a single RAF fighter had appeared to challenge them.

An armada of small craft set out from the harbour to assist the stricken convoy, which had come to a standstill. All afternoon, and into the evening, the rescue and makeshift repair work continued, and tugs stood by to tow the more badly damaged merchantmen into harbour the next day; but the Germans had not yet finished with them. In the darkness, a wave of *Schnellboote* – fast attack craft which the British called E-boats – left their bases on the occupied Channel coast and attacked the survivors. Their torpedoes sank the freighter *Elmcrest* and damaged two more vessels.

It was a grim foretaste of what was to come.

# Chapter Two

'Something's going on,' the senior controller said. 'Look there.'

Armstrong looked, peering through the soundproof glass screen at the big plotting table below, surrounded by the 'beauty chorus' – the WAAF plotters who, armed with long cues, had the task of moving indicators that showed the movement and strength of incoming raids. They were at the end of a process, unique to RAF Fighter Command, that began when the probing electronic rays of the radar stations on the coast picked up enemy aircraft assembling over France, information that was transmitted direct to HQ Fighter Command at Bentley Priory, filtered and checked for accuracy, and passed on to the Group controllers for action.

One of the WAAFs was moving, breaking what until now had been a still-life tableau. She leaned over the table and deftly pushed an indicator into position over the French port of Dieppe.

'It might be nothing,' the senior controller muttered. 'On the other hand, they might be going for the convoy.' He half-turned and spoke to an officer on his right-hand side, a flight lieutenant. 'Bring Dysoe and Dogrose squadrons to readiness,' he instructed.

'Dysoe' and 'Dogrose' were the respective callsigns of No. 74 Squadron at Hornchurch and No. 610 at Biggin Hill. On the wall display board opposite the controller's dais, red lights flicked on beside the two squadrons concerned. The flight lieutenant was speaking urgently into a telephone. His words, Armstrong knew, would create a flurry of activity as pilots headed for the cockpits of their fighters, strapping themselves in to await further instructions while ground crews stood by, battery starters plugged in, ready to supply the power that would kick the Merlin engines into thunderous life.

Armstrong surveyed the plotting board. One indicator was placed in the English Channel, just off Dover; it marked the passage of a large coastal convoy, code-named 'Bread'. It was clear the Germans knew about the convoy, for a Dornier 17 had flown over it earlier that morning as it passed the North Foreland. The Dornier had been attacked by a flight of Spitfires from Manston and badly damaged; three of its four crew had been killed when it crashed near Boulogne, but the survivor had alerted his superiors to the presence of the ships. The RAF, of course, knew nothing of the Dornier's eventual fate; the fact that it had got away was warning enough that attacks might be expected.

The senior controller twisted his head round and smilingly addressed a young WAAF who was standing just behind Armstrong. 'Time for coffee, I think, Janet. And don't forget Squadron Leader Armstrong.'

Armstrong was finding it hard to adjust to his new rank, which he had held for exactly fifteen days. It had come along with a Bar to his Distinguished Flying Cross, awarded for his service in France. His only problem was that he was, as yet, a squadron leader without a squadron to lead. He had returned to England to find himself posted missing, having lost touch with the RAF authorities in France after his photo-reconnaissance Spitfire had been shot down; he had spent several weeks with a French fighter squadron, claiming several victories in the air, before being evacuated via Gibraltar as France tottered on the brink of defeat. He had passed several days closeted in the bowels of the Air Ministry, writing lengthy Intelligence reports on everything he had seen and done on the Continent, while waiting to be given a new command. His previous one, the Photographic Reconnaissance Flight at Deanland, in Suffolk, had been absorbed in his absence into a much larger organisation at Heston, in Middlesex.

The senior controller's urgent voice interrupted his thoughts.

'There's a raid developing, all right. Twenty-plus. Better get the boys airborne. Scramble Dogrose.'

The flight lieutenant depressed a switch on the console in front of him, opening a direct landline link with Sector Operations at Biggin Hill, and passed on the order. In a remarkably short time, a distorted voice crackled over a loudspeaker high up on the wall.

'Dogrose Squadron airborne.'

'Roger, Dogrose. Patrol Dover, Angels twelve.'

Armstrong looked at the plotting board. The indicator that had been positioned on Dieppe had now moved into the Channel. A second indicator, denoting friendly fighters, was being pushed steadily away from Biggin Hill towards the coast. Armstrong could visualise the Spitfires – there would be no more than nine of them – climbing hard to reach 12,000 feet, their pilots narrowing their eyes in the glare of the sun. It was exactly 10.45 in the morning of 10 July 1940.

Armstrong had welcomed the chance to visit the Operations Room of No. 11 Group, Fighter Command. Buried underground at Uxbridge, it controlled the fighter squadrons that would be in the very forefront of battle when the expected onslaught by the *Luftwaffe* finally came. It seemed to be coming quickly now, Armstrong thought, if the activity of the past week was any indication.

The *Luftwaffe* had carried out its first daylight attacks on the English coast on 3 July. Among other targets, the forward airfield at Manston, in Kent, was attacked by a small force of Dornier 17s, which came in at low level and dropped anti-personnel bombs on the landing area. The only damage, luckily, was to a lawnmower. On the following day – the day that saw the devastating attack on convoy OA178 – the Germans began flying fighter sweeps over south-east England. The Commander-in-Chief of Fighter Command, Air Chief Marshal Sir Hugh Dowding, and the Air Officer Commanding No. 11 Group, Air Vice-Marshal Keith Park, refused to be drawn, and it was not until 7 July that there were serious skirmishes, the RAF losing six aircraft and the *Luftwaffe* five. Three of the aircraft were Spitfires of No. 65 Squadron from Hornchurch, victims of a surprise attack by Messerschmitt 109s as they climbed.

Sixty-two people were killed that night, when single German bombers attacked Godalming, Aldershot, Haslemere and Farnborough. The next morning, RAF fighters shot down two Dornier 17 reconnaissance aircraft off the south coast. During the morning, squadrons were repeatedly scrambled to meet German fighter sweeps, shooting down four Me 109s, and in the afternoon a section of 610 Squadron broke up an unescorted Dornier 17 attack on a convoy off Dover, losing one Spitfire in the process. An hour later, Hurricanes of No. 79 Squadron, taking off from Hawkinge to intercept a reported raid, ran into Me 109s and lost two aircraft. At the end of the day, the RAF had lost four aircraft, the Germans seven.

The WAAFs, all of whom were wearing headphones,

were reporting more incoming enemy aircraft. Forty-plus Germans were now heading towards Dover. Armstrong suspected that the raid was made up of fighters and bombers, in equal numbers.

The young WAAF, Janet, arrived with a tray of coffee cups. There was even a plate of biscuits. She offered the tray to Armstrong, who smiled his thanks, took a cup and ladled some sugar into it from a tin bowl. The WAAF placed the other cups carefully at the elbows of the senior controller and his deputy, neither of whom, now engrossed in the plot that was building up, took any notice.

The controller thoughtfully tapped a pencil on a notepad that lay in front of him and spoke to the flight lieutenant. 'Scramble Dysoe Squadron, John,' he said quietly, 'and bring Wagon to readiness.' 'Wagon' was No. 111 Squadron, whose Hurricanes were at Croydon. Bending forward slightly so that his lips were close to a microphone, the controller issued an instruction to the squadron that had taken off from Biggin Hill a while ago. His eyes were on the plotting board all the while.

'Dogrose, climb to angels one-six and keep your eyes peeled. Forty-plus hostiles, about twenty miles from you, angels twelve.'

Dogrose Leader acknowledged, and the controller smiled to himself. He knew perfectly well that 610 Squadron's Spitfires would already be at 16,000 feet, or somewhere near it. A former fighter pilot himself, he knew that fighter leaders operating under the control system almost always added a few thousand feet to the altitude they were given. If he had instructed Dogrose to climb to 16,000 feet initially, they would now be at 20,000. When 74 Squadron's leader reported that he was airborne from Hornchurch a couple of minutes later, the controller ordered him up to 15,000 feet; a couple of thousand feet on top of that, and he would be in a good position to deal with the German fighter escort.

Armstrong, watching intently, had already guessed the controller's plan. He had begun to give Dogrose a series of fresh headings to steer, and it was clear that he intended to manoeuvre 610 Squadron into a position from which it could attack out of the sun. As the attack developed, 74 Squadron would arrive high overhead; its pilots would be able to pick their targets out of the mêlée below.

Of course, Armstrong told himself, it wouldn't work exactly to plan. It never did. In a few minutes' time, there would be an almighty free-for-all over the Channel, a high-speed cut-and-thrust in which sheer luck would play a key part.

On the wall, the tannoy emitted a steady hissing crackle. It was broken by a shout from Dogrose Leader that made them all jump.

'Dogrose Squadron, tally ho! Thirty-plus bandits dead ahead. Sections line astern. Attack, attack!'

The tannoy continued to hiss with the effect of atmospherics. The voices of the pilots high above the Channel sounded distorted and tinny. In the Operations Room, fragmentary and disjointed sentences enabled Armstrong and the others on the dais to follow the course of the developing battle.

'Dogrose aircraft, this is Dogrose Blue Three. Look out, more fighters coming in from seven o'clock!'

'Four, six more going from two to three o'clock.'

'Bloody hell, use your callsign! Okay, I can see 'em, passing from three to four o'clock now, parallel. No panic yet. Concentrate on the Dorniers!'

'Dogrose Red Section, look out below!'

'One-oh-nines behind, watch it!'

'Aircraft four o'clock, climbing – it's okay, they're Spits.'

A new voice, calmer than the rest, broke in.

'Dysoe Leader, bandits below. Tally ho! Line astern, go!'

'Dysoe Yellow Two calling, bandits above and behind, coming down now.'

'Okay, but I can't see the bastards. Tell me when to break.'

'Got that bastard. Oh, what a beaut of a flamer!' That voice was unmistakably Australian.

'Dogrose Leader to all sections, close up. Turning starboard.'

'Hold it, hold it . . . BREAK!'

'Get stuck in, everybody.'

'Dysoe Yellow Two, break right!'

'Christ, that was close!'

The disembodied voices were taut now, charged with

the strain of air combat, of handling the speed-stiffened controls of fighters cleaving through the sky at nearly 400 m.p.h.

'Dysoe Red Section, there's half-a-dozen of the buggers right on top of you!'

'For Christ's sake get a move on, Red Three!'

'Get your own bloody finger out, that bastard nearly had me then!'

'It's okay, I'm watching your tail.'

'Dogrose Yellow One calling, can't see a bloody thing . . . oil everywhere.'

'Get the hell out of it, then!'

'Bandbox, Bandbox, this is Dogrose Leader. Bandits turning out to sea off Dungeness . . . I think they've had enough.'

The senior controller addressed his microphone. 'Understood, Dogrose. Good show. Dogrose and Dysoe Squadrons, pancake.'

That meant return to base and land. Ground crews would hurriedly refuel and rearm the Spitfires, which would then remain at readiness until the squadrons were told otherwise. The controller turned to his deputy, the flight lieutenant, and told him to scramble No. 111 Squadron. As soon as the Hurricanes were airborne from Croydon, they were ordered to patrol over Dungeness as an insurance against the enemy sending a second wave of bombers over the Channel.

But no second wave came, and the plotting board

remained empty. It was not until the afternoon that a new attack developed, and No. 111 Squadron, having landed to refuel in the meantime, were in the thick of it. One of its Hurricanes, twisting away from an attack by an Me 109, collided with a Dornier 17 and lost a wing; the RAF pilot baled out but was killed. Two of the Dornier's crew baled out and were captured; a third crew member was lost. Three more Hurricanes were damaged, but all were repairable. When the score was added up at the end of the day's combat, it was the *Luftwaffe* that had suffered the worst. The Germans lost seven aircraft, including three Messerschmitt 110s – the much-vaunted twin-engined 'destroyers' that were proving no match for the RAF's determined fighters. And the Spitfires and Hurricanes had done their work; the merchant convoy lost only one ship that day.

Armstrong, who had been following the day's events with interest, although with some frustration that he was a mere bystander, noted with surprise that it was already four o'clock in the afternoon. Another hour or so, and the controllers' shift would be ended. Lunch had consisted of some sandwiches, sent over from the Officers' Mess, and Armstrong was hungry. He was planning to spend the night at Uxbridge before returning to the Air Ministry, and was looking forward to a spot of tea, followed by a good dinner later on.

A telephone at the flight lieutenant's elbow shrilled. He picked it up, listened for a moment, said, 'Yes, sir, he is,' and turned to Armstrong, one hand cupped over the mouthpiece. 'It's for you,' he said. 'Somebody from Stanmore, a Wing Commander Baxter. Ring any bells?'

Armstrong shook his head, mystified, and took the handset. A voice on the other end of the line said, 'Squadron Leader Armstrong? This is Wing Commander Baxter, HQ Fighter Command. Thank God I've tracked you down. The AOC-in-C wants to see you, right away. I'm sending a car for you.'

The Air Officer Commanding-in-Chief was Air Chief Marshal Sir Hugh Dowding. Somebody's pulling my leg, Armstrong thought, but in the next instant realised that Baxter was deadly serious. 'Any idea what it's about, sir?' he asked.

'None at all,' Baxter told him, 'other than it seems pretty urgent. Look, wait at the Mess, will you? The car won't be long. You needn't bring any kit with you. We'll send you back to Uxbridge for the night.'

Armstrong bade a temporary farewell to the controllers and made his way to the surface via a lift, blinking in the strong afternoon sunshine as he emerged from the entrance to the underground bunker, protected by blast-proof doors and sandbags. A steel-helmeted sentry slapped the butt of his rifle and Armstrong returned the salute. After a brisk walk he arrived at the Officers' Mess and, conscious of the rumblings in his stomach, persuaded a reluctant steward to bring him some tea and toast. Afternoon tea was not until five-fifteen, and mess stewards hated to have their routine interrupted.

Stanmore was only a few miles away, and Armstrong had not long to wait before the promised car arrived. The driver turned out to be a very attractive WAAF, who saluted smartly and opened the rear door for him. He wondered if there were any unattractive WAAFs; if there were, he had never seen one. Maybe they were hand-picked by air marshals.

The pretty WAAF proved uncommunicative, either because she was shy or because she knew that silence was the best defence against predatory pilots, and Armstrong idly surveyed the scenery as the car – a Hillman – purred steadily along through Ickenham, Eascote and Hatch End towards its destination. Eventually, the WAAF turned the vehicle into the spacious grounds of Stanmore Park, on the edge of which stood Headquarters, RAF Fighter Command. The headquarters were located in an impressive mansion called Bentley Priory, the site taking its name from a religious house founded in 1170 by Ranulf de Glanville, Chief Justiciary of England. The present building, dating from 1777 and designed by Sir John Sloane, had been successively the property of the Marquess of Abercorn; Lord Aberdeen, Prime Minister of England in the mid-nineteenth century; the dowager Queen Adelaide, widow of William IV; and a railway engineer called Sir Hugh Kelk, who had turned it into an hotel. His other claim to fame was that he had built the Albert Memorial in Hyde Park, free of charge to the nation. From 1902 to 1924 the Priory had been used as a girls' school, and after that it became the property of the Royal Air Force.

The onset of war had scarred Bentley Priory. Important offices were protected with piles of unsightly sandbags, trenches were dug, beautiful trees were cut down to provide an all-round field of fire, and the entire white stucco building was sprayed with green and brown camouflage paint. The majestic clock tower was painted black, as were many of the windows, and a fine conservatory was pulled down to make way for temporary office accommodation for the operations staff. Starting in January 1939, a massive hole, forty-two feet deep, was dug just to the east of the priory; 58,000 tons of earth were removed and replaced by 17,000 tons of reinforced concrete, which formed the various rooms of the underground operations centre. When this was fully installed, the earth was replaced over it, forming a shield that no bomb would penetrate.

This was the nerve centre of RAF Fighter Command. It was completed on 9 March 1940. Just a month later, German forces invaded Norway. A month after that, they attacked France, Belgium and Holland. Now they were poised to attack Britain itself.

The man at the hub of the spiders-web of communications that controlled every fighter squadron in Britain sat at his desk. Armstrong saluted with all the crispness he could muster as he was ushered in by a much-beribboned group captain, and waited. Air Chief Marshal Sir Hugh Dowding glanced up at him over the top of half-moon spectacles, grunted, and returned to the document he was reading. Armstrong remained at attention and waited, covertly studying the man in front of him, the man with a burden of responsibility second only to the Prime Minister's. The AOC-in-C, he thought, looked exactly like the headmaster of a leading public school. He was staid in appearance, which probably accounted for his nickname of 'Stuffy'. The impression was closer to the truth than Armstrong imagined, for Dowding had been considerably influenced by his father, a successful prep school headmaster and a man of strict Victorian values.

Queen Victoria had still been on the throne when Hugh Caswall Tremenheere Dowding had joined the Army in 1899 after an education at Winchester. Unable to gain acceptance as an engineer, he became a gunner, and for the next ten years served in a succession of British garrisons around the world.

At the age of thirty-two, shortly before the outbreak of the First World War, he learned to fly at Brooklands and gained his pilot's licence. His father found out, and furiously ordered his son to give up what he considered to be a dangerous pastime. Dowding obeyed, but not for long. In 1914, he went to Belgium with the Royal Flying Corps; by 1915 he was a squadron commander, and by 1918 a brigadier, commanding a Group of the newly-formed Royal Air Force at Henley. In the 1930s he became the Air Member for Research and Development, supervising the technological advances – such as radar – which were to prove so vital in just a few years' time.

In July 1936, aged fifty-four, he was appointed Air Officer Commanding-in-Chief of RAF Fighter Command, and set up house with his sister just along the road from his office at Bentley Priory. And in four short years, he turned the United Kingdom's air defence system into the finest in the world, pulling together all its essential components: radar, communications, fighters, group commanders who were his personal choice and who would conduct the day-to-day running of the battle that was now starting to develop.

Dowding gave another subdued grunt and carefully laid aside the papers he had been studying. He picked up a buff-coloured folder and began to study it. Almost as an afterthought, he said: 'Sit down, Armstrong. I shall not be a moment.'

Armstrong removed his cap and did as he was told, resisting an urge to relax too much and cross his legs. The headmaster image intensified; he felt as though he were about to receive six of the best. The chair on which he was gingerly perched was lit by a shaft of slanting sunlight; it stood close to the large windows, which faced south, and the afternoon was not yet far enough advanced to plunge Dowding's study – Armstrong could not bring himself to think of the room as an office – into shadow. Bentley Priory stood on a rise, and Armstrong, glancing out of the corner of his eye, saw that the study commanded a fine view of the grounds.

'It seems you have seen quite a bit of the world since the War began, Armstrong.'

Armstrong jumped, startled by the sudden comment. Dowding was staring at him fixedly. Without waiting for a response, the Air Chief Marshal glanced at the buff folder again. Armstrong knew that it was his record of service.

'A good deal of photographic reconnaissance experience,' Dowding continued, as though talking to himself. 'And I have your preliminary report on your experiences in France. You know your way around Europe. What night flying experience do you have?' Oh, God, Armstrong thought, and said: 'Very little, sir. We sometimes took off before first light and landed after dark on PR operations, but that's about all.'

'No matter.' Dowding looked hard at the younger man. 'Armstrong, I shall come to the point. I want you to form a squadron. A specialist squadron that will take the war to the enemy. I will allocate six Blenheims to it initially; I can spare no more than that for the moment. Its task will be to attack the enemy's airfields by day and night, and above all to destroy bombers. The Blenheims will be the Mark IV fighter version, and your initial operating base will be Bircham Newton. You will need to set up your own facilities there, but you will have my full personal authority. I shall arrange for the posting in of experienced crews from other Blenheim squadrons in Fighter Command, but you are free to select your own flight commanders. The Blenheims will arrive within the week and I want you operational within three. Time is not on our side, Armstrong. The station commander at Bircham Newton will be expecting you. That will be all.'

In a state of bewilderment, trying hard to prevent his mouth from falling open, Armstrong muttered something, rose to his feet, replaced his cap and saluted. On the way back to Uxbridge he hardly noticed the WAAF driver. His mind was preoccupied with all sorts of problems associated with his new and unexpected appointment, and the first of them was that he had no idea where he was going to start.

# Chapter Three

Armstrong decided that the logical place to start would be Bircham Newton, and the next day, after putting his kit together and telephoning the Air Ministry to explain what he was up to, he went along to the Uxbridge Motor Transport Pool and commandeered a car and a driver to take him there. The airfield lay a few miles north-east of the royal residence of Sandringham, close to the Wash, and the fact that Bircham Newton was a Coastal Command station did nothing to ease his perplexity.

He got the driver – an airman, this time – to drop him at the Officers' Mess and then dismissed the man, who went off for some lunch before driving back to Uxbridge. Armstrong signed the 'warning in' book at reception and was shown to a vacant room by a mess steward, then went off in search of the station commander. In fact, the station commander found him first, or more correctly they found one another, almost colliding on the Mess steps.

Armstrong apologised and stepped aside, then spotted the four rings of blue rank braid on the other's sleeves, hurriedly introducing himself before the group captain vanished inside the Mess. They shook hands in the doorway.

'I know about you,' said the station commander, whose name was Crosby. 'Come and have some lunch, old man, and we'll talk. I really don't know why you've been sent here rather than to a Fighter Command station. I don't even know what you'll be flying.'

Armstrong told him, and Crosby's face brightened. 'Oh, that's it, then. We've got a Blenheim fighter squadron here already. Number Two-three-five, transferred from Fighter Command. Arrived last month. No problem with spares and servicing. I'll introduce you to their CO later on; he's out on a job at the moment.'

Over lunch, carefully avoiding any mention of what the role of Armstrong's squadron was to be, Group Captain Crosby told Armstrong what the Bircham Newton squadrons had achieved in the War so far. The 'resident' squadron, he learned, was No. 206, which at the outbreak of war had been equipped with Avro Ansons. The squadron had flown reconnaissance missions off the northern coasts of Holland and Germany, ranging as far as the Elbe estuary – an area Armstrong knew well from his photo-recce days – and in April 1940 it had re-equipped with American-built Lockheed Hudsons, with which it had carried out bombing attacks on Rotterdam after the German invasion of the Low Countries in May. At the time of the evacuation of Dunkirk, the squadron had put every available Hudson into the air to conduct battle flights over the English Channel, skirmishing several times with enemy fighters.

By that time the first Blenheim fighter squadron, No. 254, was stationed at Bircham Newton, its main task to protect the fishing fleets operating off East Anglia, a job that had recently been taken over by No. 235 Squadron after 254 left for Hatston in the Orkneys to defend the naval base at Scapa Flow against German raiders from Norway. To avoid congestion, the Blenheims sometimes used the grass airfield at Docking, a few miles up the road.

After lunch, Group Captain Crosby took Armstrong for a tour of the aerodrome in his staff car. Bircham Newton dated from the First World War, having been built in 1916 for use as a training station. In the summer of 1918 the RAF's first heavy bomber squadrons had formed here, equipped with big Handley Pages that were capable of bombing Berlin, but the Armistice had been signed before they had a chance to do so. It had remained a bomber station until its transfer to Coastal Command in 1936, and after that it had expanded greatly, with new hangars and accommodation being built. It was a comfortable, well-appointed station, and Armstrong was impressed.

The favourable first impression lingered right up to the

moment when Crosby's car drew up beside a run-down wooden building that stood not far from one of the magnificent 'C' Type aircraft hangars that had been built in the 1930s. It reminded him of one of the shacks at Deanland, where his photo-recce flight had been based. Crosby's next words threatened to send him into a state of mild depression.

'This will be your dispersal. Treat it as temporary; it's the best we can offer for the moment. I'll get some painters in tomorrow. Freshen the place up a bit. Needs a telephone as well. Care to take a look inside?'

'No, thank you, sir,' Armstrong said. 'Actually, I could do with making a few phone calls, just to get things moving.'

'No trouble,' Crosby told him. 'You can use one of the offices in Station HQ. The padre's, in fact. He's away on leave. We are rather wishing he was back. Not so much for spiritual guidance, you understand. His room in the Mess is full of bottles of home-made wine and the hot weather is making the corks pop. Nobody can find a key and the smell is awful. God only knows what sort of a puddle is in there.'

Armstrong asked the group captain to drop him at the Mess. Crosby obligingly waited while he went up to his room and retrieved a folder from among his personal effects, then they drove to Station Headquarters, following a straight road with barrack blocks on one side and the parade ground on the other. Armstrong didn't quite know what to make of the station commander; a tall, balding man whose medals betrayed his service in the last war, he seemed affable enough, but Armstrong had the impression that he would be merciless with anyone who crossed him.

The padre's office was neat and tidy, with a clear desk top and not a crucifix in sight. After thanking Crosby, Armstrong closed the door, opened the window – for it was uncomfortably warm in the room, which had obviously been without an airing for several days in the padre's absence – and sat down at the desk, opening the folder. It contained the names and current locations of various people. He ran his finger down the list, picked up the telephone and asked the switchboard operator to place a Service call to Leconfield, in Yorkshire. The girl said that she would call him back. Some fifteen minutes later the telephone bell spoke stridently to him, and he was able to speak to the Leconfield operator.

'Good afternoon,' Armstrong said. 'Would you put me through to the Polish Flight, please? My name is Squadron Leader Armstrong.'

A few moments later, a very un-Polish voice that belonged to a Flight Sergeant McGregor answered his call, and Armstrong asked to speak to Captain Kalinski. After another short delay, there came a shout down the line that threatened to deafen him.

'There is only one bloody Armstrong who would want to ring me up! Is that you, Ken? And what is this squadron leader business? You must have friends in high places.'

'Seems like it, Stan. Listen, I have a job that might interest you, but it might mean treading on a few toes. Can't talk about it over the phone. Can we meet up?'

Stanislaw Kalinski did not hesitate. In just a few short months the two men had become firm friends, starting with the day their paths had crossed in Norway. By an amazing coincidence their paths had crossed again in France, where Kalinski and many of his countrymen were serving with the French Air Force, and they had got out of that country together when the French campaign collapsed in ruins. Armstrong had learned from his Air Ministry contacts that Kalinski was in temporary command of a newly formed Polish Fighter Flight at Leconfield; it would shortly be expanded into a full squadron, and the Pole would relinquish his post to a Royal Air Force officer. That was a prospect, Armstrong knew, that would not appeal to him one bit.

'Where are you?' Kalinski wanted to know. Armstrong told him.

'Bloody hell!' the Pole roared. His command of English had become very colloquial. 'That's practically next door! I will fly there at once.'

'Steady on, Stan,' Armstrong cautioned. 'You'll need some sort of authority.'

'Bugger authority,' Kalinski responded cheerfully. 'For the time being, I'm the authority. I will be there in one hour. Meet me at the Watch Office.'

The Watch Office stood on the edge of the concrete

apron, jutting out like a small promontory, overlooking the expanse of the aerodrome. It was a square, brick building surmounted by the control tower, with a signals square laid out in front of it. The square displayed all the information, such as the direction of landing, that the pilot of an aircraft that was not fitted with radio might need. The building that housed the fire tender and the Fire Section Office stood nearby.

Two deckchairs were placed by the edge of the signals square, one of them occupied by a flight sergeant who was gazing at the eastern sky through binoculars. He failed to notice Armstrong until the latter sat down in the other deckchair, then looked embarrassed and began to stand up, hastily buttoning up his tunic as he did so. Armstrong told him to stay put and asked him what he was looking for.

'The Blenheims, sir,' the other told him. 'They should be back shortly.' Armstrong saw that the man wore an observer's half-wing on the left breast of his tunic. 'Your squadron?' he queried. The flight sergeant nodded.

'Yes, sir. Two-three-five. I would have been out with them, but for this.'

He indicated his right foot, which Armstrong now noticed was encased in plaster. 'Fell off my bike,' the flight sergeant added ruefully, by way of explanation. Armstrong smiled, and asked him if he had seen much action.

'Not since Holland,' the NCO told him. 'That was pretty rough. We were sent over to shoot up the Junkers transports that had landed on the beach near The Hague, and we attacked Rotterdam airport a few times. That cost us two or three crews. We've been carrying out shipping searches since then, and convoy protection.' He broke off suddenly and looked at Armstrong, eyeing his medal ribbons.

'Looks as though you've seen a fair bit yourself, sir. Are you just posted in?'

'In a manner of speaking,' Armstrong said absently, his attention taken by a distant speck in the sky. 'Is that one of your Blenheims?'

The flight sergeant raised the binoculars, and a moment later gave a grunt. 'Yes, that's them all right. One, two, three, four, five . . . that's odd.'

'What is?'

'Well, sir, I'm sure we only sent three aircraft out.' He shrugged. 'Maybe the other two are somebody else's aircraft, coming in to refuel. Care to take a look, sir?' He passed the binoculars to Armstrong.

The pilot looked, giving the focusing knob a slight touch, and the incoming aircraft leaped into sharp relief. There was no mistaking the front view of the Blenheim, with its deep fuselage, almost square in cross-section and flanked by the two radial engines, and the marked dihedral – the upward sweep – of the outer wing sections.

But there was something subtly different about the two aircraft bringing up the rear. Their fuselage cross-sections were more rounded, with a little blister underneath.

Armstrong needed no second glance. He had seen that view before in Norway, coming down at him in a 60-degree dive. He was out of his chair in a split second, binoculars abandoned, heading at a run for the door of the watch office. 'Junkers eighty-eights!' he yelled over his shoulder at the startled flight sergeant. 'Take cover!'

Armstrong took the watch office stairs three at a time and burst into Flying Control, where an elderly flight lieutenant and a corporal WAAF sat at the console. A pair of binoculars stood at the flight lieutenant's elbow; Armstrong grabbed them and thrust them into the bewildered officer's hand.

'Take a look at the rearmost aircraft,' he said urgently. 'They're Ju eighty-eights! Those Blenheim gunners must be asleep!'

The flight lieutenant peered through the glasses and gave a gasp. 'My God, you're right! Edith, sound the alarm. No time to call operations – use the emergency siren.'

The WAAF hurried out onto the balcony and began to crank the handle of a siren that was fixed to the rail. Its raucous note wailed out over the airfield. No more than forty-five seconds had elapsed since Armstrong had first identified the enemy aircraft.

The controller seized the microphone and spoke crisp instructions into it.

'Redwing aircraft, do not pancake. I repeat, do not pancake. You are being shadowed by two Huns. Tell your gunners to wake up!'

There was a moment of silence, then a garbled acknowledgement crackled over the radio. Almost instantly, the two outermost Blenheims broke hard left and right while the third remained on course, diving steeply to gain speed until it was speeding only feet above the far boundary of the airfield.

Armstrong bounded back down the stairs and ran out into the open, looking around him with some vague notion of finding a fighter aircraft which he might commandeer, but seeing no likely candidate. The flight sergeant, he saw, had abandoned his deckchair and was hobbling as fast as he could towards a sandbagged slit trench near the Fire Section.

The Blenheim that had come down to low level howled overhead, so low that he could smell hot oil emanating from its Bristol Mercury engines. Of the other two, there was no sign. He could hear the two incoming Ju 88s now; their Jumo engines produced an altogether different sound from the Blenheim's, a throbbing snarl that seemed charged with menace. In another half-minute they would be overhead, and from the course they were following Armstrong deduced that they were intent on unloading their bombs on the hangars. Quickly deciding that discretion was the better part of valour, Armstrong made a beeline for the slit trench into which the flight sergeant had disappeared.

Suddenly, he stopped dead in mid-stride, almost twisting an ankle as a new sound cut through the Junkers' drone.

It was a sound he knew well, the scream of a high-powered Rolls-Royce Merlin going full belt. He looked towards the German bombers, which were now looming large.

A shadow flashed over him, and a blast of slipstream plucked at him. A Hurricane zipped past, going like a bullet, heading full tilt for the Ju 88s. Its eight machine-guns chattered, their noise blending into a continuous snarl, like a huge piece of cloth being torn.

Completely unnerved by what was apparently a suicidal head-on attack, the pilots of the two Ju 88s went into steep climbing turns in opposite directions, much as the two Blenheims had done a little earlier. Armstrong, rooted to the spot, had a clear view of the bombers' pale blue undersides.

The Hurricane shot between them like a lightning bolt, climbed steeply for several thousand feet, rolled as it climbed, and then went over on its back, diving vertically. With beautiful timing the pilot recovered from the half-loop, made a high-g low-level turn that must have pulled most of the blood from his head, and came in behind the left-hand Junkers, which together with its companion was roaring eastwards at about 1,000 feet. The Hurricane's guns hammered once more and smoke streamed from the bomber's starboard engine. Its bomb doors opened and Armstrong counted four bombs dropping clear; a few moments later they exploded somewhere beyond the airfield boundary. The Ju 88 and the pursuing Hurricane vanished behind the geysers of smoke and dirt, and then the Hurricane reappeared, climbing hard again. It turned and went after the second Junkers, the two aircraft fading rapidly into the distance, heading towards the coast.

The clouds kicked up by the bomb-bursts gradually subsided. Beyond them, a mushroom of oily smoke rose slowly into the sky, marking the Junkers' grave. The aerodrome suddenly came to life, the activity starting with the fire tender, which emerged from its shelter and raced off round the perimeter track. The flight sergeant with the injured foot scrambled out of the slit trench and stared at the pall of smoke, a look of awe on his face.

One by one, the three Blenheims came in to land, their radial engines chugging as they taxied slowly to their dispersals. Armstrong watched the crews disembark. A few minutes later, a black dot in the north-eastern sky resolved itself into the silhouette of the Hurricane; it made one circuit of the airfield and then it too made its approach to land, touching down lightly on the runway in use. As it turned on to the perimeter track Group Captain Crosby's staff car rolled up to the Watch Office and the station commander got out. He spotted Armstrong and came over, pointing towards the taxying fighter.

'I want to meet that chap,' Crosby said. 'I really do!'

A little while later he got his wish when the Hurricane came to a stop on the concrete near the Watch Office. Two ground crew hurried up and placed chocks in front of its wheels as the pilot gave the engine a final burst of power to clear any oil from the plugs and switched off.

Crosby and Armstrong approached the fighter as the pilot climbed from the cockpit and slid off the wing, flexing his legs a little as his feet touched the ground. He ripped off his flying helmet, and Armstrong grinned. Stanislaw Kalinski, red in the face, was swearing fluently in a mixture of Polish and English.

He spotted Group Captain Crosby and broke off in mid-expletive, bringing himself to attention and giving a small bow. 'Kalinski,' he said simply. Crosby shook his hand.

'Good show!' he said. 'First-rate effort! I take it the other Hun got away?'

'Yes, sir. Bloody bugger! I ran out of ammunition. I hit him a few times, though. Maybe he will go into the drink. Good afternoon, Ken,' he added, in much the same breath, thrusting out his hand again.

Crosby looked from one to the other, raising an eyebrow. 'You two know each other, then?'

'Yes, sir,' Armstrong said. 'It's because of me that Captain Kalinski is here, actually.' He gave the group captain a brief résumé of the situation, and the reason for the Pole's visit.

'Well, I'm damned glad you turned up when you did, Captain,' Crosby said. 'I don't think it's stretching a point too far to congratulate you on saving my airfield.' He eyed the smoke on the horizon. 'I'm going over to take a look. Care to join me?'

Armstrong and Kalinski both declined. They knew what

they would find: a smoking crater surrounded by burning wreckage and overhung by a pall of sickly odour, the smell of burning aluminium; and somewhere among it all, bloody chunks plastered with clods of earth, the remains of men no older than themselves. They had seen it all before.

Crosby nodded understandingly. 'Right, then. See you in the Mess at teatime.'

'Which isn't far off,' Armstrong observed as the station commander's car pulled away. 'Come on – I'll take you over to our dispersal hut, and I'll tell you all about it as we go.'

By the time they reached the dispersal, Kalinski knew as much about their forthcoming mission as Armstrong did. He was enthusiastic about it, and keen to join the team, although he was less than enthusiastic about the type of aircraft they would be flying.

'Something faster and more heavily armed would be better,' he said. 'Hurricanes, perhaps. They could be fitted with extra fuel tanks. Or what about this new machine I've heard about, what's it called? Oh, yes. The Whirlwind. It's in the latest aircraft recognition charts.'

Armstrong had seen it too, or rather photographs and silhouettes of it. Built by Westland Aircraft, the Whirlwind was powered by two Rolls-Royce Peregrine engines and was reputed to have a top speed of over 350 m.p.h. It also had an impressive armament of four 20-mm cannon.

'Funnily enough, I was talking to a chap in the Ministry about that just the other day,' he told his companion.

'Apparently there have been some problems with its engines, and it'll be quite some time before it's fully operational. It's undergoing trials with Two-six-three Squadron at Grangemouth, up in Scotland, at the moment. And I don't think that anybody has even considered hanging long-range tanks on a Hurricane yet, so it looks as though we're stuck with the Blenheim. I know you've flown with an air gunner before, but that's something I'm going to have to get used to.'

They arrived at the dispersal hut, and Armstrong saw that the door was open. Through it came the sound of someone whistling tunelessly. Puzzled, he went inside, closely followed by Kalinski.

A lanky, bespectacled man wearing the uniform of a pilot officer was standing awkwardly on a step ladder, pinning a large map to the wall. His back was to the newcomers, and Armstrong coughed to attract his attention. The man half-turned, dropping a handful of drawing pins, and almost fell off the ladder. He climbed down, peering short-sightedly at Armstrong's badges of rank, and drew himself up to something approximating a position of attention. Armstrong suppressed a grin; the man looked rather like a bent hairpin.

'And who might you be?' the pilot enquired mildly. When the other spoke, it was with a slight stammer.

'Squadron Leader Armstrong, sir? I'm Briggs, your squadron adjutant. Sorry about this, sir.' He bent down to retrieve the drawing pins.

'Don't worry about it,' Armstrong told him. 'Well, Briggs, you're news to me, but I'm glad to have you aboard.' He introduced Kalinski, who regarded Briggs with an expression of faint amusement. 'It'll be good to have someone to handle the paperwork,' Armstrong added.

'Er . . . yes, sir. Speaking of which . . .' Briggs crossed the room and picked up a fat buff folder from a table top. The folder was stuffed with forms. 'This is for your attention, sir,' the new adjutant said apologetically. 'It's mostly the details of the aircrews who are being posted in, but there are some forms you have to sign. To do with requisitioning equipment, sir. The telephone is on top of the list.'

He looked owlishly at Armstrong, and gave a sudden disarming grin. Armstrong grinned back, then laughed out loud, struck by the humour of the situation. For the moment, the three of them, and one dilapidated hut, comprised the total assets of the Intruder Squadron.

Well, he thought, still chuckling, it wasn't much. But at least it was a start.

# Chapter Four

*Well, now, the Germans are dive-bombing a convoy at sea. There are one, two, three, four, five, six, seven German bombers – Junkers eighty-sevens – there's one going down on its target now. Bomb – no, there – he's missed the ships . . . he hasn't got a single ship. There's one coming down with a long streak.*

*You can't see these fighters very coherently for long. You just see about four twirling machines and you hear little bursts of machine gun fire, and by the time you've picked up the machine they've gone —*

*There's a dogfight going on up there – there are four, five, six machines, wheeling and turning round. Hark at the machine guns. Hark, one, two, three, four, five, six . . . now there's something coming right down on the tail of another. Here they go – yes, they're being chased home and how they're being chased home! There are three Spitfires chasing three Messerschmitts now —*

*'Oh, boy! Look at them going. And look how the Messerschmitts*

*— oh this is really grand! And there's a Spitfire just behind the first two — he'll get them! You've got him, pump it into him. Pop-pop-pop — Oh boy, oh boy, he's going down! Oh yes — oh boy! I've never seen anything as good as this . . . the RAF fighter boys have really got these boys taped!'*

*BBC Correspondent, Charles Gardner*
*Cliffs of Dover*
*14 July 1940.*

Armstrong sat in his office and fretted. The office, and for that matter the rest of the dispersal hut, smelled of fresh paint, thanks to the efforts of Briggs and the small working party of airmen he had assembled; the windows had been cleaned and the front door now fitted properly. Even the stones that lined the path leading up to the door had been whitewashed.

Armstrong threw a heap of paperwork into the 'out' tray on his desk and sighed. Over the Channel, the Spitfires and Hurricanes of Fighter Command were tangling with the *Luftwaffe* almost every day; so far, the Germans were sending over only small formations to attack the Channel convoys, but the pattern of their operations was clear. The plan was to draw Fighter Command's squadrons into action, possibly over a period of several weeks, and weaken them as much as possible before the main assault; but Air Chief Marshal Dowding had seen through the scheme and refused to commit his squadrons to convoy protection in large numbers, contenting himself with reinforcing key coastal airfields and increasing fighter cover only when a convoy was passing through the perilous waters of the Dover Straits.

Despite the enforced inactivity – the first of the promised Blenheims and their crews had yet to arrive – Armstrong had not been idle during the past few days. He had made a meticulous study of all available Intelligence information, including reconnaissance photographs, of the German-occupied airfields in northern France and the Low Countries, and had already worked out an approximate target list, with the airfields at Lille-Nord and Arras at the top of it. According to the latest information, the Heinkel 111s of KG 53 were based at the former, and the Dornier 17s of KG 2 at the latter, and the photographs he had seen – brought back by reconnaissance Spitfires – indicated that both were densely crowded.

He had also, thanks to the good offices of No. 235 Squadron, been thoroughly checked out on the Blenheim Mk IVF, finding it a surprisingly pleasant and responsive aircraft to fly. Although the Intruder Squadron would be equipped with the earlier Mk IF, the only real difference between the two was that the Mk IVF had a longer nose, incorporating a navigator's station, and uprated Bristol Mercury engines. Both fighter versions of the Blenheim were armed with four fixed forward-firing .303 machine guns, mounted in a gun pack occupying a space in the lower fuselage normally taken up by the bomb bay, a single Vickers 'K' .303 machine gun in the power-operated turret on top of the rear fuselage, just behind the wing, and a Browning .303 mounted in the port wing.

Armstrong considered the armament no more than adequate for the task in hand, and he positively disliked the Blenheim's escape arrangements: the crew got into the aircraft by climbing onto the wing and then through a hatch on top of the fuselage just behind the pilot's seat, and they had to get out the same way, which probably explained why very few Blenheim crews had escaped with their lives when their aircraft were hit during the Battle of France.

The Blenheims that would shortly (Armstrong fervently hoped) be delivered to the Intruder Squadron would not be carrying navigators, which he did not mind; he already knew his way around north-west Europe, and it would not be long before the other crews did too. The presence of a rear gunner, novel though it was to him, was comforting in a way; at least he would not have to check the area behind his tail continually, although he was aware that the Blenheim had a vulnerable blind spot behind and beneath the tail where an attacking fighter could not be seen.

Armstrong had been reading up on the successes enjoyed by the Blenheim night-fighters so far, and it was not an impressive record. The squadrons that used them – and there were only half a dozen at the time of the German invasion of France and the Low Countries – had several skirmishes with the *Luftwaffe* during night patrols along the French coast, but had ended up with little to show for it. One crew of No. 604 Squadron had shot a Heinkel 115 floatplane down into the Channel one night in June, in conditions of brilliant moonlight and excellent visibility, but that was about it. Still, Armstrong consoled himself with the thought that an airfield would be easier to find than a lone enemy aircraft, although it would be a damn' sight more heavily defended.

There was a tap at the door and Briggs came in, bearing a cup of coffee. Armstrong eyed him with mock apprehension. 'What, more paperwork, Briggs?'

The thin adjutant smiled. 'No, sir. Not for the moment. But I've got a body for you, instead.'

'A body?' Armstrong showed his perplexity.

'Yes, sir,' Briggs explained, 'the first of our gunners has just rolled up. Sergeant Kershaw.'

'Oh, right.' Armstrong rummaged around on his desk top, searching for the file that contained the personal documentation of all the incoming aircrews. Briggs pointed it out; the telephone was resting on it.

'Oh, yes, thanks,' Armstrong muttered, opening the folder. 'Well, I'd better see him. Send him in, would you?'

A few moments later a smartly-dressed NCO came into the office and gave Armstrong a crisp salute. The pilot pointed at a chair and studied Kershaw as the latter removed his forage cap and sat down, then turned his attention to the file again.

'Kershaw, Philip Douglas,' he said. 'You're a regular airman, I see.'

'Yessir. Joined in nineteen-thirty, when I was fifteen. I was a Brat, sir,' he added proudly.

'So I see,' Armstrong said, smiling. Kershaw meant that he had been a Royal Air Force apprentice; that scheme had been founded in the early nineteen-twenties by Air Chief Marshal Sir Hugh Trenchard, the RAF's first Chief of the Air Staff (the 'father' of the RAF, as many called him), hence the nickname of 'Trenchard Brats' bestowed by the rest of the Air Force on the hundreds of young men who had passed through the system since then. Trenchard's aim, in those days of stringent economies immediately after the Great War – years in which he had been largely responsible for saving the new-born RAF from extinction – had been to provide the Service with a nucleus of thoroughly-trained technicians. Disciplined and thorough, masters of their respective trades, they were already showing their worth in this new war.

'You were an engine fitter,' Armstrong stated, reading from Kershaw's record, 'and you volunteered for flying duties in nineteen-thirty-seven. Let me see . . . operational service with Number One-one-four Squadron in France. That was the first Blenheim squadron, wasn't it?'

Kershaw nodded. 'Yes, sir. I joined the squadron at Wyton last autumn and then went to France with it. My crew was one of the lucky ones. Most of the squadron was wiped out on the day after the German invasion, and those of us that were left carried out attacks on enemy armoured columns until there was nobody left at all. I mean, we didn't have any airworthy aircraft.'

Kershaw spoke quietly. He was a Yorkshireman, a native of Scarborough, with pleasant square-cut features and brown hair, brushed straight back and with a severe centre parting.

'Why did you volunteer for this job?' Armstrong asked suddenly.

Kershaw hesitated for a moment, then said, 'Well, sir, to start with, the crew I'd been with for a long time was split up, so when the word went out that people were calling for night-fighter volunteers I thought I'd have a go.' He smiled. 'I thought to myself, it'll make a change to shoot at other people, rather than just sit there and wait to be shot at.'

'As good a reason as any,' Armstrong commented. He closed the file with a snap. 'All right, Kershaw, glad to have you. You'll be assigned to a pilot in due course.'

The air gunner stood up and fumbled with his cap, looking embarrassed. Armstrong noticed his discomfiture and asked if anything was wrong.

'Well, sir . . . it's just that the adjutant thought you might like me to crew up with you. Being the first to arrive, and with a few operations under my belt, like.'

Armstrong smiled, raising his eyebrows. 'Did he now? Well, I don't mind that at all, so long as you realise you'll be drawing the short straw. I have exactly ten hours on Blenheims, so I'll be learning as I go along. Do you still want to take the risk?'

Kershaw beamed at him. 'Not half, sir! And thanks very much. When do we get to fly, sir?'

'As soon as we've got an aeroplane, Sergeant, and don't hold your breath waiting for it to arrive. Off you go, then.'

Kershaw replaced his cap and saluted, then turned on his heel and left the office. A moment later, Briggs stuck his head around the door. There was a triumphant smile on his face.

'I've managed to track him down, sir,' he told Armstrong. 'The officer you want for your other flight commander, I mean.'

Armstrong shot out of his seat. 'Excellent! Come on then, where is he?'

Briggs consulted a piece of notepaper in his hand. 'He's at a place called St Merryn,' the adjutant informed Armstrong. 'It's in Cornwall,' he added somewhat unnecessarily, for the name could hardly fit any other part of Britain. 'Apparently he's in charge of an air target-towing unit.'

'Is he, now?' Armstrong reached for the telephone. He had a feeling that he was about to make someone in the Admiralty furious.

Half an hour later, Armstrong emerged from his office with a broad smile on his face. 'Right-oh,' he said. 'It's all fixed. Nice to have friends in high places. Come on, Briggsie; you and I are going flying.'

The adjutant stared at him aghast. 'F . . . f . . . flying, sir? But I've never been in an aeroplane in my life! I'm an administrator.'

'Well, then, it's high time you found out how the other side lives,' the unsympathetic Armstrong told him. 'Let's get you fixed up with a flying overall and a parachute. I've arranged to borrow the Station Flight's Magister. We're off on a nice little jolly to the West Country. It will take us about three hours. If we set off now, we should be there in time for a spot of lunch.'

While the highly reluctant Briggs went off to the parachute section to master the intricacies of that life-saving item of equipment, Armstrong plotted the cross-country course to St Merryn, folded the map carefully and placed it in the pocket of his overall, obtained a route forecast and the necessary clearances for the flight, and went to check out his aircraft, calling at the parachute section en route to collect Briggs and his own parachute.

The parachute section, a low building that stood just behind the station workshops, was only a short walk from the Bellman Aircraft Shed that housed the Station Flight, the function of which was basically to provide communications and liaison. It was equipped with two aircraft, a twin-engined de Havilland Dragon Rapide and the Miles Magister, which Armstrong was about to use.

The Magister, known affectionately and predictably as the 'Maggie', was the RAF's first monoplane trainer, and had been in service since 1937. It had two open cockpits, positioned in tandem, one behind the other, and was powered by a 130-horsepower de Havilland Gipsy Major inline engine. It cruised at about 100 m.p.h. and would do 130, flat out. At cruising speed, it would fly for around three and a half hours before its fuel ran out.

Armstrong signed for the little aircraft and then walked around it, carrying out his preflight checks and explaining to Briggs what he was doing. Afterwards, he made Briggs strap himself into his parachute and saw that the pale-faced adjutant was safely installed in the rear cockpit and firmly belted in before climbing into his own cockpit. There wasn't much room, much less than in the RAF's other basic trainer, the Tiger Moth.

An airman swung the propeller and the Gipsy Major came alive. Armstrong watched the cockpit instruments settle down on the vibrating panel, their indicator needles all in the right places, then picked up the Gosport speaking tube – the only means of communication between front and rear cockpits – and asked Briggs if he could hear him all right. A muffled voice answered in the affirmative.

A few minutes later they were airborne, climbing steadily towards the south-west. Armstrong levelled out at 3,000 feet, checking his map to make sure he was on track, and settled down to enjoy the flight. As the Magister purred on its way, he pointed out landmarks to his passenger, who despite his earlier misgivings also showed every sign of enjoying himself. The morning was clear and sunny, with the shadows of a few fleecy fair-weather cumulus clouds chasing each other across the countryside below, and visibility was perfect.

Their route took them close to Northampton, and a

few miles away to the south-east they could see Tiger Moths doing circuits and bumps at Denton aerodrome, recently opened as a relief landing ground for Sywell. They flew on over Oxfordshire and into Gloucestershire, revelling in the sunshine, but Armstrong did not allow himself to relax too much; this was flying training country, with student pilots blundering around the sky. As though to emphasise the point, a twin-engined Airspeed Oxford trainer, camouflaged on top and painted bright yellow underneath, passed a couple of hundred yards to the left, going in the opposite direction; it turned behind them and Armstrong saw it lower its undercarriage, apparently heading for the airfield at Little Rissington, in the heart of the Cotswolds.

A while later the River Severn came into view, glistening over to the right and broadening into the expanse of the Bristol Channel. South Wales was clearly visible on the other side. They flew over the smoky expanse of Bristol, smelling coal and sulphur and temporarily losing the sun behind a pall of industrial haze, and then the welcome brightness returned and there was water below the Magister's wings as Armstrong took it directly over Bridgwater Bay.

The Quantock Hills and Exmoor lay beyond and Armstrong map-read carefully as they flew over the moor's expanse. The hilly nature of north Devon meant that there were no airfields that could be identified on this sector of the route, but it didn't matter; he could see

Barnstaple Bay over to the right and he altered course slightly in that direction. They were building an airfield over there, on the site of North Devon Airport, and from what he could see work was well advanced. It was going to be a big aerodrome, too, with three concrete runways.

Keeping the coast just off his starboard wingtip he flew steadily on, answering as best he could the flow of questions that came over the Gosport tube. Briggs's earlier nervousness had vanished completely and the bespectacled adjutant seemed to be revelling in his newfound experience. Armstrong decided that if he ever took Briggs flying again, he would provide him with a map so that he could identify landmarks for himself.

The pretty Cornish town of Padstow came up ahead, and he located his destination airfield without difficulty, some three miles further on. Its four new runways gleamed in the sunshine, and he made out the rectangular shapes of large hangars. There didn't appear to be any activity in the circuit, but he picked out the cruciform shapes of several aircraft on the concrete apron.

Armstrong descended to 2,000 feet and flew overhead, looking down to check the wind direction. There was only a light wind blowing from the south, and as he turned downwind it did not add appreciably to the Magister's ground speed. There was no sign of a green light from the tower, authorising him to land, but on the other hand no red flares warned him off, so he turned across wind and lined himself up on the approach, pulling on the lever that lowered the little aircraft's flaps and heading towards the ground at a steady 65 m.p.h. He flared out just right above the runway and made one of the best three-point landings of his flying career.

'All right, Briggsie, we're down. You can open your eyes now. Don't get out just yet, though,' he joked, as he taxied the Magister carefully towards the hangars, weaving the nose from side to side to improve the view ahead.

He brought the Magister to a stop and switched off the engine. Two men wearing dark blue overalls emerged from a hangar and thrust chocks under the wheels, then stood back, watching as Armstrong and Briggs unfastened their seat and parachute harnesses and climbed from the respective cockpits, the former with the ease born of practice, the latter awkwardly, holding on to his glasses with one hand.

One of the naval ratings – for such they were – stepped forward, looking uncertainly from Armstrong to Briggs. 'Squadron Leader Armstrong, please?' he queried.

'I'm Armstrong,' the pilot informed him. The rating nodded affably at him. 'Very good, sir. Would you come with me, please?'

Armstrong looked around him as they walked, gazing at the aircraft parked nearby. There was a Blackburn Skua fighter/dive-bomber, which he recognised at once – he had seen plenty of them in the Norwegian campaign – and another aircraft identical to a Skua except for a four-gun turret fitted just behind the pilot's cockpit. 'Wonder what that is?' he said aloud.

'It's a Blackburn Roc, sir,' Briggs informed him casually. 'And that biplane on the other side of it is a Blackburn Shark.'

Armstrong stared at him. 'Well, Briggs, your aircraft recognition is better than mine.' Briggs gave him a thin smile.

'It's a bit of a hobby of mine, sir. Just because I'm a 'wingless wonder' doesn't mean I'm not interested in aeroplanes. I might even get to like flying in them, thanks to you.'

The naval rating led them to a small, single-storey office block next to one of the hangars. Inside, a corridor with highly polished linoleum underfoot ended at a green door which bore a wooden plaque with the words: Lt J. Baird, DSC, OC TT Flight. The rating knocked, then stepped aside to allow Armstrong and Briggs access to the office on the other side.

A stocky, red-haired man whose uniform sleeves bore the gold braid of a naval lieutenant rose from behind a desk and advanced to meet Armstrong. Briggs looked on with interest as the two greeted each other warmly, and waited his turn to be introduced. Lieutenant Jamie Baird, known to his friends as 'Dickie', grasped Brigg's hand firmly. When he spoke, Briggs detected the lilt of the Western Isles in his voice.

'Welcome to the last place God made,' he said, 'and do

sit down, the two of you. It's very good to see you, Ken. I must say, your call came as a bit of a surprise. Now, what's this all about? Better still,' he commented, glancing at his watch, 'you can tell me over lunch. You can leave your flying overalls here.'

The two men stripped off, smoothing the creases out of their uniforms, and went with Baird to the Wardroom. The terminology at St Merryn, Armstrong learned, was pure Royal Navy; even the ground staff talked about going for a 'run ashore' to Padstow. He learned, too, that St Merryn had not yet been officially commissioned by the Admiralty; that was due to happen next month, when the establishment would be called HMS *Vulture*.

'What you see is what we've got,' Baird said as they walked to the Mess, waving his hand at the three parked aircraft. 'As a matter of fact, the Shark isn't ours; the silly sod of a pilot landed here thinking that it was St Eval, a few miles down the road near Newquay. We're treating him to lunch before he goes off to face a bollocking.'

Armstrong discovered that the airfield, once it was fully operational, would be used to train the majority of the Fleet Air Arm's fighter pilots, and the fleet of target-towing aircraft would be expanded to full squadron strength.

Briggs already knew about Baird. The naval officer and Armstrong had first met during the days of the 'Phoney War', when Baird was instructing RAF personnel on ship recognition; their paths had crossed again in April 1940, when Baird was flying Skuas on operations over Norway

— the same campaign that had brought Armstrong into contact with the third point of the triangle, Stanislaw Kalinski. Baird told the two RAF officers that he had also flown Skuas operationally during the Dunkirk evacuation, operating out of Manston. The Fleet Air Arm fighters, completely outclassed by the Messerschmitts, had suffered heavy losses. After that, Baird had been awarded the Distinguished Service Cross and sent for a rest to St Merryn, where his job was to establish the target-towing flight.

Over lunch, Baird listened intently while Armstrong told him about the Intruder Squadron he had been asked to form, then leaned back in his chair, chewing thoughtfully on a mouthful of cold beef. He swallowed, took a sip of water, then said, 'I must say I'm tempted, Ken. Very tempted. And I know one or two Fleet Air Arm pilots who've been seconded to RAF fighter squadrons, so I expect some strings could be pulled. The only thing that worries me — two things, actually — is that firstly I have no twin-engine experience, and secondly that I might not fit in as a flight commander. The chaps might not take too kindly to a Navy type giving them orders.'

Armstrong grinned. 'As to the first point, I didn't have any twin experience either, until about a week ago. Neither did the other flight commander; in fact, he's ploughing around the sky in a Blenheim even as we speak. What counts is combat experience, and all three of us have that. You'll have no trouble with the troops, believe me.'

He did not mention that, apart from Sergeant Kershaw, he had yet to meet 'the troops'; he was expecting them before the end of the week. He could only hope that they showed as much keenness and promise as his gunner. It was impossible to tell from the personal records he had seen so far. Everything seemed all right on paper, but you never could tell.

'Do you want to think about it overnight, and let me know?' he asked.

Baird dug his fork into another piece of meat and shook his head, smiling. 'No, Ken. I've thought about it. How soon do you think you can have the paperwork in order, and get me out of this place?'

Ignoring the curious stares of the few other diners, Armstrong reached out and clasped Baird's hand. The Intruder Squadron was about to get off the ground.

# Chapter Five

*Thursday, 8 August 1940*

For several days now, there had been a lull in the air
fighting over the English Channel, but the pilots of
Fighter Command had seen plenty of combat before
that. The Command's blackest day so far had been 19
July, when ten RAF aircraft had been shot down against
a claim of only four German. Six of the RAF aircraft
had been Boulton Paul Defiants of No. 141 Squadron,
from RAF West Malling, which were bounced by Me
109s off Dover and shot down in flames one after the
other. Only one crew escaped. The Defiant, with no
forward armament and only four machine-guns in a
power-operated turret, was proving easy meat for the
German fighters.

The last days of July had seen several engagements
over the Straits of Dover, and the entry in the war diary

of one fighter squadron – No. 32, flying Hawker
Hurricanes from Biggin Hill in Kent – was fairly typical:

*20 July 1940. Convoy escort, ten miles east of Dover. At 17.58
hours, with 610 Squadron, intercepted a raid on the convoy by
about about fifty Junkers Ju 87s and Messerschmitt 110s, escorted
by Messerschmitt 109Es. Led by S/L Worrall the Squadron shot
down six of the enemy (three Me 110s, two Me 109s and one Ju
87) and damaged four others (all Me 109s). One Hurricane was
lost but the pilot, F/Lt Bulmer, is reported to have baled out near
North Foreland. Sgt Higgins was slightly wounded in the face by
splinters from bullets striking his protective armour.*

It all sounded very optimistic, and the young pilots of
No. 32 Squadron would doubtless have been astounded
to learn that, in the heat of a whirling air battle, they had
scored no victories at all. No Me 110s were lost on operations, and the five Me 109s confirmed as destroyed were
attributed to other fighter squadrons. Nor did the *Luftwaffe*
lose any Ju 87s, although four made forced landings. In
all, the Germans lost fourteen aircraft on 20 July, the RAF
nine fighters.

On 25 July the *Luftwaffe* had adopted a change of tactics,
sending out strong fighter sweeps to draw the RAF fighters
into battle before launching its bomber attacks. As a conse-
quence, sixty Ju 87 Stukas were able to bomb a convoy
with impunity while the fighters of No. 11 Group were
on the ground refuelling. Later in the day, the convoy was

attacked by thirty Ju 88s, escorted by about fifty Me 109s. The attacks continued until 18.30; fifteen of Dowding's fighter squadrons were engaged in the course of the day, destroying sixteen enemy aircraft for the loss of eight of their own, all Spitfires. As for the convoy, eleven out of its twenty-one ships were sunk by dive-bombers or by *Schnellboote* that came out of their lairs to torpedo the survivors.

In four weeks of operations over the English Channel, the *Luftwaffe* had sunk 40,000 tons of British shipping, including three destroyers. Combat losses during the month's air fighting were *Luftwaffe* 190, RAF Fighter Command 77, of which 46 were Hurricanes – the aircraft which had borne the brunt of the fighting, and would continue to do so. Fifty RAF fighter pilots were killed or missing, and with German preparations for the invasion of England clearly under way, the loss was serious.

Then came the lull. It did not last for long.

*

Off the Dutch Coast, 13.00 Hours

The Blenheim's Bristol Mercury engines roared healthily in Armstrong's ears, the glittering arcs of their propeller blades just a few feet away on either side of the glazed cockpit. Four thousand feet below, the sea was a glassy sheet of blue and grey and green, flecked with white foam. Fifty miles away off the Blenheim's port wingtip, somewhere behind a hazy horizon, was the long sweep of the Dutch coast, curving from the Zuider Zee to The Hague.

Also invisible in the haze, stretched out at intervals between his own aircraft and the Norfolk coast, were eleven more Blenheims – five of his own squadron and five of No. 235. It was the Intruder Squadron's first operation, and although it was not the kind of mission for which it was intended, Armstrong felt elated. He now had a full complement of six aircraft and eight crews, all worked up to operational standard, and soon they would be roving over north-west Europe in search of the enemy.

Today's operation, however, was dictated by an urgent situation. Creeping down the English coast towards the Thames estuary was convoy CW9, code-named 'Peewit': twenty-five colliers, laden with 40,000 tons of coal and coke, the tonnage required every week to keep industry going in the South. While the fighter squadrons of No. 11 Group stood by to protect it as it reached the narrowest part of the Channel, the two Blenheim squadrons from Bircham Newton were to sweep the seas to the north, on the alert for marauding E-boats – as the British called the fast and heavily-armed *Schnellboote* – and enemy destroyers that were rumoured to be lurking in Dutch harbours, ready to put to sea.

Armstrong called his gunner over the intercom. 'See anything, Kersh?' He knew that if Kershaw had spotted anything he would have informed his pilot at once, but the call helped to relieve the monotony that was setting in. They had already been on patrol for ninety minutes, flying a fixed route, turning on a reciprocal course every half-hour, and all they had seen so far was empty sea.

'Not a thing, skipper,' the gunner replied. He had been constantly swivelling his turret from side to side, scanning the sky as well as the sea, wishing that they might come upon one of the Heinkel floatplanes that patrolled as far as the East Anglian coast. As well as the He 115 mine-layers, RAF Intelligence had deduced that the Germans were also using Heinkel 59 air-sea rescue aircraft for reconnaissance, so these were fair game too, unless they were found in the actual process of rescuing shot-down airmen. The RAF's suspicions had been confirmed when, early in the morning of 11 July, an Avro Anson of No. 217 Squadron, based at St Eval in Cornwall and out on patrol over the Channel, had sighted a Heinkel 59 bearing a civilian registration and flying suspiciously close to a coastal convoy. The Anson had damaged it and forced it down into the sea. Its four-man crew took to their dinghy and were later picked up drifting near the Channel Islands; the aircraft was retrieved by the Royal Navy and brought ashore at Walmer Harbour in Kent.

Armstrong thought for a moment, then made up his mind. 'All right,' he told Kershaw. 'I'm going in closer to the enemy coast. Keep your eyes peeled.'

He swung the Blenheim's nose round through ninety degrees, studying his map as he did so. He had been navigating as precisely as possible, working out his position by mental dead reckoning, using the techniques he had practised so often during his time as a Spitfire photo-reconnaissance pilot, making long and solitary flights deep into Germany. His new course would lead him to the island of Walcheren, and the estuary of the River Scheldt.

The haze persisted, making it difficult to see more than a few miles ahead. He flew steadily on for ten minutes, keeping to the same altitude. The glare of the sun on the mist was beginning to hurt his eyes.

Suddenly, the haze ahead, slightly off to the right and close to the surface of the sea, seemed to thicken, as though someone had flicked a blob of ink into the middle of it. He called Kershaw.

'Take a look at our two o'clock, down low,' he instructed. 'What do you reckon?'

There was a pause while the gunner moved his turret round, then he replied, 'Smoke, skipper. I'm pretty sure it's smoke.'

'Okay, let's take a look. I'm going down a bit.'

He swung the aircraft's nose a few degrees to the right and began a gradual descent, striving to make some visual sense of what lay ahead. Then he saw the ship. He had studied enough recognition photographs to identify it immediately as a *Wolf*-class destroyer. It was moving at speed, and behind it came two larger vessels which he did not recognise. He thought they might be fast minelayers, and they were followed by two more destroyers, spaced out a little way on either flank, so that the whole formation resembled an arrowhead. The ships were heading south-west, and to Armstrong that meant they were a threat to the convoy.

Breaking radio silence, he called the other Blenheims and gave them the ships' present position. As he did so, flak started to come up thick and fast from the leading destroyer. She was the *Jaguar*, and she was armed with four 20-mm anti-aircraft guns. Armstrong was heading straight towards her; the Blenheim, head-on, was presenting the smallest possible silhouette to the German gunners, and he knew that to turn away now would mean exposing the aircraft's vulnerable underside to them. Crouching low in the cockpit and feeling very naked, he doggedly held his course, descending to 500 feet. The destroyer leaped to meet him and he opened up with his forward armament, seeing his small-calibre bullets churning a path of foam across the water and kick flakes of paint from the destroyer's hull. Then the Blenheim was howling over the ship's superstructure and he heard Kershaw's solitary gun chattering as the gunner raked her decks.

Armstrong held the Blenheim low over the sea and counted to twenty, then pulled the aircraft up in a steep climbing turn that had the startled Kershaw temporarily staring down into the water through the perspex cupola of his turret. Armstrong levelled out, searching for the enemy convoy, and found it at once; all three destroyers were now pumping shells at him, spattering the sky with black puffs of smoke, but he was out of range.

Armstrong began to circle the ships at a safe distance, continuing to transmit their position, course and speed, hoping that the other Blenheims – some of which had acknowledged his call – would reach the scene quickly, particularly the 235 Squadron aircraft, which were armed with 500-lb bombs. He knew that the German radio intelligence service would have picked up his transmissions, and that enemy fighters were probably on their way to protect the ships at this moment.

Two Blenheims arrived and joined him. He saw by their code letters that they belonged to his squadron; one was flown by Dickie Baird, the other by a flight sergeant pilot called Van Berg, a powerfully-built South African who – or so he said – had come over from his native land for two reasons, one of which was to fly reasonably modern aircraft. So far, he had not explained what the other reason was.

Armstrong instructed both pilots to keep clear of the convoy, and to look out for enemy fighters while they awaited the arrival of the 235 Squadron boys. They did not have to wait for long. The first three bomb-carrying Blenheims came sweeping in at low level from the north-west within five minutes, attacking in line abreast. They made their run over the German ships unscathed. Armstrong watched their bombs drop away, two from each aircraft; five missed, raising waterspouts as they detonated, but the sixth exploded on the stern of one of the minelayers – if such they were – in a flash of flame, followed by a cloud of yellow smoke. The ship began to lose way almost immediately.

The remaining Blenheims came up, and soon the sky over the German ships resembled a beehive, with the Mk 1F fighters prowling defensively around the fringes while the last three bombers attacked in their turn through the flak bursts, which looked like the spatterings from a flicked paint brush. The enemy ships were now taking evasive action, all except the one that had been hit earlier, and the two leading Blenheims in the second flight missed their targets. The third, some distance behind, singled out the damaged and smoking ship and planted its bombs squarely into its superstructure, racing overhead and jinking away across the sea, pursued by tracer shells from one of the escorting destroyers.

For long seconds nothing happened; then the ship erupted in a tremendous explosion that tore her in two, a great pillar of flame rising from her centre section. The shock wave of the blast was clearly visible in a ring of vapour, expanding outwards with incredible speed. Then came a secondary explosion and a geyser of smoke and debris that hid the shattered vessel from sight. Metal plates whirled crazily through the air and smacked down into the sea.

Armstrong was still watching the scene of devastation in horrified fascination when a yell over the R/T alerted him to danger.

'Watch out for fighters! Fighters in the sun, high. Four Messerschmitts!'

Armstrong raised his hand, peering into the sun's glare between his outstretched fingers, and almost at once picked out the fighters, their wingtips dragging short condensation trails as they turned hard overhead before curving down to make their attack. He pressed the R/T button on his control column and urgently radioed his pilots, using the callsign that had been allocated to them.

'Moonshine aircraft, one-oh-nines coming down hard. Turn into the attack. Meet them head-on!'

He pushed the throttles wide open and climbed to meet the Messerschmitts, which were arrowing down in two pairs, one behind the other. Over the radio, he heard 235 Squadron's leader call up his own pilots, telling them to form up and head for home, keeping low down. That way, there would not be room for a Messerschmitt to manoeuvre itself into position to make an attack from the blind spot under the tail.

The two leading Messerschmitts came down on Armstrong like a whirlwind and he opened fire, grey smoke trails spearing out from the Blenheim's ventral gun pack towards them. The Blenheim shuddered with the recoil of its guns, and through the vibrating windscreen he saw the enemy fighters' noses twinkling with orange flashes as they fired in turn. There was a sudden almighty bang and a large hole appeared in the perspex of the cockpit, on the right-hand side, followed a split second later by another bang as a cannon shell made its exit through the cockpit floor. Then the Messerschmitts streaked past him in a blur, one on either side, and Kershaw's gun chattered as he took a swift shot at one of them.

Frantically, Armstrong looked for the other pair of enemy fighters, but could see no sign of them. He came out of the climb, throwing the Blenheim into a series of steep 'S' turns, but still could not locate the 109s. In the far distance he could see the 235 Squadron aircraft, in tight defensive formation, heading for the English coast, and decided prudently that it was time to follow suit.

He ordered his pilots to form up and descend to sea level, feeling relief when all five of them acknowledged. He wondered why the 109s had broken off the attack, and it was Kershaw who solved the mystery.

'Spitfires at eleven o'clock, skipper. Nice timing, I'd say.'

Armstrong, who had been forced to pull his goggles down over his eyes to shield them from the gale that howled through the shattered windscreen, peered up and to the left. There they were, the familiar shark-like shapes: six of them, in two neat flights of three, turning protectively overhead. God bless Twelve Group's controllers, Armstrong thought fervently, who had seen fit to despatch the fighters to their aid.

All the Blenheims returned safely to base with no more than minor damage: two or three had collected splinter holes, and Armstrong's aircraft would need a fair bit of repair work to patch up the holes where the cannon shell had passed through. His was the only aircraft to have been hit by an enemy fighter; he did not dwell on what would have happened if the shell had deviated from its path by just eighteen inches. The hole in the right-hand side of the windscreen was exactly on a level with his head.

There was much excitement and back-slapping among the newly returned crews, several of the air gunners claiming excitedly that they had hit a Messerschmitt. Armstrong, standing quietly off to one side and smoking his pipe, exchanged glances with Kalinski and Baird; they knew perfectly well that the gunners hadn't hit a thing. So, apparently, did Kershaw, who shook his head and smiled. He had probably come closer than anyone else to hitting one of the speeding fighters, and he knew perfectly well that he had missed.

The next morning, Armstrong learned from the station Intelligence officer that the enemy ships they had attacked had indeed been on a minelaying expedition to the south-western area of the North Sea. The fact that they were carrying out the operation in broad daylight, with all the risks that entailed, indicated that something really big was in the wind. Similar minelaying operations had been carried out by fast patrol boats and aircraft off the Channel ports west of Dover. It appeared that the Germans were intent on sealing off the Channel in a bid to prevent heavy warships of the Royal Navy, based at Scapa Flow and in the Clyde, from reinforcing the light cruisers and destroyers based in the Channel area. It all pointed to the possibility that the Germans were going to attempt an invasion sooner, rather than later.

Armstrong also learned the fate of the Peewit convoy. Attacked first by Stukas, and then after dark by E-boats, it had been ravaged. Despite the efforts of Fighter Command – its pilots taking part in the heaviest air fighting so far, with up to 150 aircraft involved in the battles that raged between the Thames estuary and the Isle of Wight – the convoy had lost seven ships sunk and a dozen damaged. The cost to the *Luftwaffe* on that August day was thirty-one aircraft; the RAF lost twenty precious fighters.

Later that day, Armstrong received a signal from HQ Fighter Command. The Intruder Squadron was to move at dawn on 10 August to RAF Manston in readiness for offensive operations against the enemy.

Manston, Kent. The foremost airfield of No. 11 Group – the very forefront of the battle that was to come.

# Chapter Six

*Directive No.17 for the Conduct of Air and Sea Warfare Against England*

*In order to establish the necessary conditions for the final conquest of England I intend to intensify air and sea warfare against the English homeland. I therefore order as follows: the German Air Force is to overpower the English Air Force with all the forces at its command, in the shortest possible time. The attacks are to be directed primarily against flying units, their ground installations, and their supply organizations, but also against the aircraft industry, including that manufacturing aircraft equipment . . .*

*Adolf Hitler*

\*

*Calais-Marck Airfield, France,*
   *Monday 12 August 1940*
   'Come on, Falcke, mount up. It's nearly time to go.'

# THE INTRUDERS

*Leutnant* Hans Lehmann clapped his wingman, *Feldwebel* Joachim Falcke, on the shoulder and ground the stub of his cigar into the ground before climbing onto the wing of his Messerschmitt 109E. The familiarity between officer and NCO did not seem out of place between these two; Lehmann and Falcke had been through a great deal together from the day war broke out, first of all defending the skies of northern Germany against daylight raids by British bombers – a phase that had not lasted long, because the Tommies had suffered horrendous losses before switching their operations to the hours of darkness. They had fought in the skies of Norway, and a month later they had battled against French fighters over the Maginot Line, that useless fortification that had not even slowed down the German offensive in France, the *Blitzkrieg* – lightning war – that had brought the German armies to the Channel coast in less than a fortnight.

As he swung a leg into the Messerschmitt's cockpit, Lehmann glanced at another fighter parked fifty metres away – the aircraft of the group commander, *Hauptmann* Walter Rubensdorffer. He was the leader of Special Group 210, the only one of its kind in the *Luftwaffe*. It had been formed specifically to carry out fast precision attacks on small targets, and to this end it was equipped mainly with twin-engined Messerschmitt 110s, fitted with special racks to carry 250-kg or 500-kg bombs. One flight – commanded by Lehmann – had Me 109s, and its function was to escort the slower and less manoeuvrable 110s. The fighter-bomber tactics had been tried out for the first time a couple of days earlier, when the Me 110s had dive-bombed a large British convoy south-east of Harwich, setting two large transports on fire.

Lehmann counted himself lucky to have been selected to command Special Group 210's fighter flight, and luckier still to have been permitted to bring Falcke along with him. Falcke was a superb pilot and a crack shot, and if his background had been different he would almost certainly have been an officer. But giving commissioned rank to those of the lower social order was not the style of the class-conscious military hierarchy, although Lehmann knew only two well that some of the high-ups who styled themselves as belonging to high-bred 'Prussian stock' were nothing of the sort; they had wormed their way into power with the rise of the Nazi Party and added a 'von' to their names. He couldn't help chuckling at the thought of his own name, Lehmann, which meant 'vassal'. Somewhere along the line, his ancestors must have dragged themselves out of the mire. At any rate, his father was a much respected lawyer.

A white flare arced into the sky, the signal for the Messerschmitts to start their engines. There were thirty aircraft in the group, but only twenty – twelve Me 110s and eight 109s – had been detailed for this mission.

The pilots – and, in the case of the two-seat Me 110s, the gunners too – had already been in action earlier in the day. Early in the morning, fifteen Me 110s had bombed the curious masts on the British coast at Dover, Pevensey and Rye, which *Luftwaffe* Intelligence experts knew were used by the RAF to locate German aircraft and direct their fighters to intercept them. The attack had not been particularly successful; although some damage had been caused to all three masts, the German radio listening service had detected transmissions only three hours later which indicated that the British stations were fully operational again. It had been a different story at Ventnor, on the Isle of Wight, which had been attacked by fifteen Ju 88s; their bombing was extremely accurate and the station was damaged beyond repair.

While these attacks were in progress a force of Dornier 17s raided the RAF airfield at Lympne with showers of 50-kg bombs, causing some damage to the tarmac, hangars and buildings. Attacks on the British convoys in the Channel also continued; shortly after 12.00, twenty-two Junkers 87s dive-bombed a convoy in the Thames estuary north of Margate, scoring hits on two tramp steamers.

Now, at 13.30, it was once again the turn of Special Group 210. Lehmann watched as the Me 110s took off first; the faster 109s would catch up with them over the Channel. Then he was leading his own flight out to the take-off point, swinging the Me 109's nose into wind, holding the stick back as he slowly opened the throttle. He gave the thumbs-up to Falcke, on his right, and relaxed his backward pressure on the stick, at the same time releasing the brakes. The Messerschmitt surged forward and the tail came up almost immediately, giving Lehmann a clear view along his take-off run past the long cowling that concealed the 1,150 horsepower Daimler-Benz DB601 engine and the two 7.9-mm MG 17 machine guns that lay on top of it. Lehmann's 109, a brand-new E-4 model, also had two 20-mm cannon in the wings; some of his flight were still equipped with the earlier E-3 model, which in addition to its machine guns had a single cannon firing through the propeller shaft.

The Me 110s were already dots in the distance, and Lehmann's flight climbed hard to catch up with them. His intention was to position his fighters several thousand feet higher up, so that he would be in a good position to dive on any RAF fighters that tried to pounce on the fighter-bombers. But he would not climb until the last moment; if he did so too soon the British radio direction-finding stations would pick up his aircraft, and the low-flying Me 110s would be robbed of their element of surprise.

It was a beautiful afternoon, and a haze of heat shimmered over the white chalk cliffs that marked the English coast. It was time to climb now; even if the English picked up the incoming formation, it would have completed its mission and be on its way home again before the Spitfires or Hurricanes arrived to challenge it.

Glancing over at Falcke, he waggled his wings and then jabbed a finger towards the sky, making his intentions clear without breaking radio silence. The signals division of RAF Intelligence, the 'Y' Service as the British called it, was very good at picking up radio transmissions for German aircraft and alerting Fighter Command. Falcke waved a hand in acknowledgement and the two Messerschmitts pointed their noses towards the blue vault above, followed by the remainder of the flight.

The coast was directly below their wings now as they levelled off at 12,000 feet. The Me 110s were slipping inland like a school of sharks, thundering over the roof-tops of the seaside town of Ramsgate as they headed for their target.

Idly, as he looked down, Lehmann wondered why the Messerschmitts had not been ordered to make another attack on the British radio-location stations, which were surely a key factor in the RAF's air defence system. It would have made more sense than their present mission – a low-level attack on the RAF fighter airfield of Manston.

Armstrong was in the briefing room at Manston, poring over maps with Baird and Kalinski and working out the finer details of the mission the Intruder Squadron would be flying that night, when the sirens began their banshee wailing. Almost immediately, the airfield's anti-aircraft defences opened up.

For a second the three officers stood frozen, then they dashed outside, Armstrong tossing the briefing room keys to a startled duty airman with a shouted instruction to make sure the room was locked up and the keys returned to the security of the guardroom. Outside, the three of them piled into Baird's battered Austin Seven, a mode of transport in which Armstrong had had the misfortune to be a passenger on several previous occasions. As they did so, the distinctive shape of a Messerschmitt 110 roared past at hangar roof level, its mottled grey camouflage glistening in the sun. They clearly saw the heads of the two crew.

'Step on it, Dickie! Make for our dispersal!' Armstrong yelled. The naval officer obliged, taking the car careering around the perimeter of the grass airfield, dodging fire tenders and other vehicles that were dashing to and fro. Bombs seemed to be going off all over the place, sending fountains of dirt and smoke high into the air. More Messerschmitts came tearing through it, followed a few moments later by three Spitfires, climbing hell for leather. They were the Spits of No. 65 Squadron, which had been about to take off when the raid developed. Three more flights of Spitfires also managed to lurch off the ground between the bomb bursts; miraculously, only one of them came to grief when a bomb blast right in front of it reversed its propeller and stalled the engine. The aircraft smacked back on to the ground and slewed to a stop in a cloud of dust and clods of earth, damaged but repairable. The pilot jumped out unhurt and made for the dubious sanctuary of the nearest hole in the ground, of which there were now plenty.

The Intruder Squadron's Blenheims were dispersed in sandbagged revetments on the far side of the airfield, and as Baird drew up Armstrong noted with relief that they seemed to have escaped damage. Nearby, there was an anti-aircraft position mounting a twin Lewis gun; someone behind it was blazing away at the attackers and Armstrong saw that it was Kershaw, an expression of fierce concentration on his sweating face. He ceased firing as Armstrong came up; the Me 110s had gone, the last of them passing over the airfield like a tornado.

Not all of them had got away. A heap of twisted wreckage lay in the middle of the devastated airfield, licked by crackling flames. The body of a German airman lay nearby, minus its legs. The other crew member was roasting in the ruined cockpit.

'Look out!' Kalinski shouted. 'More of the bastards!' He threw himself prone on the ground and was instantly imitated by Armstrong and Baird. Kershaw dived back behind his gun and swung the twin barrels in the direction of the new threat. Travelling at incredible speed in two sections of four, eight Me 109s raced low over the airfield, cannon and machine-guns blazing, their outlines obscured by the smoke. Then they were gone in a thunderclap of sound before anyone had a chance to fire a shot. Armstrong craned his neck and caught sight of them in the distance, climbing like arrows.

'That's buggered the job,' Baird said matter-of-factly, getting to his feet and brushing bits of grass from his uniform. He stood with his feet planted wide apart, hands on hips, staring at the wreck of the aerodrome.

Armstrong let out a long breath. 'It is a bit of a mess,

I'll admit,' he said. 'Looks like the sods have done us again, Stan.'

Kalinski gave a non-commital grunt, his brows knitted. Like Armstrong, he had been on the receiving end of German air attacks too often. 'Can't wait to give them a taste of their own medicine,' he said.

'I'm afraid you're going to have to,' Baird pointed out. 'Nothing's going to fly from here for a bit. They've well and truly plastered the place.'

He was right. They could all tell at a glance that Manston would not be fit for operations that day, nor perhaps even the next. But although the surface of the airfield was badly cratered, the Spitfires – all except the one damaged by the bomb blast – had escaped unscathed. From the ground, it appeared that the German fighter leader had completely misjudged the speed of his attack, throwing away the chance of engaging the climbing Spitfires; in fact, Lehmann, his view of Manston obscured by the swirling clouds of dust and smoke, had not realised that any of the Spitfires had got airborne, and had ordered his pilots to make a single fast strafing run. By the time he noticed the Spitfires he was shooting past them, and as he climbed hard, intent on turning to attack them, someone brought his attention to more Spitfires, coming up fast from the north-west. With his 109s outnumbered now by two to one, Lehmann prudently decided to head for home.

Other RAF airfields had been hit that day. Lympne was the first to suffer, receiving a carpet of 140 bombs before breakfast. The bombers and their escorts were engaged by the Spitfires of No. 610 Squadron, which shot down two Me 109s for the loss of one Spitfire, whose pilot baled out. One of the Messerschmitts, harried by Spitfires, crashed into a hill near the village of Elmham. There was no sign of the pilot, but his body was found later, in a field six miles away. He had survived the crash and crawled from the wreck, only to succumb to his wounds as he tried to reach the coast.

Lympne was attacked by a second wave of Dorniers in the afternoon, after station personnel had made valiant efforts to tidy up the mess in readiness for an inspection by the RAF's Inspector General, Air Chief Marshal Sir Edgar Ludlow-Hewitt. 'First bombs, now bullshit!' one disgruntled shovel-wielding airman was heard to remark. The attack came in a few minutes after Ludlow-Hewitt arrived, and he was confined to an air raid shelter while the airfield was plastered from end to end by Junkers 88s and Dornier 17s. He wisely decided to postpone his inspection for a few days.

After Lympne and Manston, it was the turn of Hawkinge, near Folkestone. At 16.30 its fighter squadron – No. 32, flying Hurricanes – took off to replace No. 610 on patrol. As they cruised over Margate, Hawkinge was dive-bombed by Ju 88s, taking the airfield defences completely by surprise. Most of the bombs cratered the airfield, but one stick fell on the technical site, flattening two hangars, workshops and domestic buildings and setting fire to others. Five of No. 32 Squadron's Hurricanes, low on fuel, managed to land between the bomb craters.

At Manston, Armstrong and his crews joined ground personnel and soldiers who had been drafted in, working throughout the night to fill in bomb craters. By dawn, the work was complete and the workers, officers and men alike, breakfasted on thick bacon sandwiches and steaming mugs of tea provided by the NAAFI and the ever-present Salvation Army before staggering off exhausted to snatch whatever sleep they could.

As they did so, cypher experts working under a cloak of the strictest possible secrecy at a place called Bletchley Park were in the process of deciphering a top secret German code message that had been intercepted. It was a simple message, but to the codebreakers it was dynamite.

*From* Reichsmarschall *Goering to all units of Air Fleets 2, 3 and 5. Within a short period you will wipe the British Air Force from the sky. Heil Hitler.*

It was the signal for the launching of *Adler Angriff,* the 'attack of the eagles' – the massive air assault that was to be the prelude to a full-scale invasion of southern England.

# Chapter Seven

*Eagle Day: Tuesday, 13 August 1940*
Since before dawn the Luftflotten had stood poised to launch their onslaught, but at the last minute H-hour was postponed because of bad weather. The Dorniers of KG 2, however, failed to receive the signal in time; they took off in fog and rain and set a course over the Channel without fighter escort. The fifty-five bombers were tracked by radar and Air Vice-Marshal Keith Park, commanding No. 11 Group, immediately scrambled two squadrons of Hurricanes and a squadron of Spitfires, dividing them between the damaged airfields at Hawkinge and Manston and a convoy in the Thames estuary. He also ordered most of a squadron of Hurricanes to patrol between Arundel and Petworth, leaving behind one section to cover their home base of Tangmere, near Chichester. Lastly, a squadron of Hurricanes orbiting over Canterbury could

be called upon to support any of the other units engaging the enemy. Further west the commanding officer of No. 10 Group, Air Vice-Marshal Quintin Brand, scrambled a squadron of Hurricanes to patrol the Dover coast. Another squadron and a half of Hurricanes was held on immediate readiness at Exeter.

Flying in tight formation, just under the cloud base, the Dorniers droned over Eastchurch airfield and unloaded their bombs on the runways, hangars and parked aircraft. At that moment the raiders were attacked by the Spitfires of No. 74 Squadron from Hornchurch, led by Squadron Leader 'Sailor' Malan. One of the bombers dived vertically into the ground; the remainder climbed hard towards the clouds to escape the dogged fighters. Then the battle was joined by the Hurricanes of No. 151 Squadron under Squadron Leader John Gordon, followed a few minutes later by the Hurricanes of No. 111 led by Squadron Leader John Thompson, and a fierce air battle developed over the Thames estuary. By the time the bombers reached the sheltering cloud five more had gone down in flames. It was just after 08.30.

Two hours later, twenty-three Me 110s of the LG 1 Group took off from their airfield near Caen with orders to patrol the south coast near Portland. Although they were picked up by radar as they crossed the French coast near Cherbourg, and although their strength was correctly reported as 'twenty-plus bandits', there was one thing the radar 'eye' could not tell: the type of aircraft it was tracking.

Since Dowding had given orders that his Spitfires and Hurricanes were to avoid combat with enemy fighters if possible, and concentrate on the bombers, the sector controllers of No. 11 Group would probably not have scrambled any fighter squadrons had they known the identity of the enemy aircraft. In the event, three fighter squadrons took off from Tangmere, and in doing so fell into the very trap Dowding had been trying to avoid. The Germans planned that when their bombers finally arrived they would catch the Hurricane and Spitfire squadrons on the ground as they refuelled and rearmed.

The Hurricanes engaged the Me 110s over the coast and the German fighters immediately adopted a defensive circle. Three Hurricanes were forced to break off the action with battle damage, but five 110s went down into the sea and as many more staggered back to France with such severe battle damage that they were either scrapped or put out of action for several days. The action highlighted the heavy, twin-engined Me 110's inferiority in combat with lighter, more manoeuvrable fighters, and to make matters worse LG l's mission had failed. The unit had drawn three British fighter squadrons on to itself so that the bombers could slip through according to plan – but somewhere along the line the plan had gone badly awry, and the bombers did not come for another three hours. By that time, the RAF fighter squadrons were ready for them again.

At 15.00, fifty-two Junkers 87 dive-bombers of *Stuka-*

*Geschwader* 77 under Major Graf Schonborn took off from their base at Flers to attack RAF airfields near Portland. They were escorted by the Me 109s of *Jagdgeschwader* 27. However, southern England was now hidden under a blanket of cloud, making a dive-bombing attack out of the question, and the Stukas circled over the coast in search of a target. Within minutes their fighter escort was being hotly engaged by a strong force of Hurricanes from Exeter and Middle Wallop, while fifteen Spitfires of No. 609 Squadron attacked the bombers. Five of the Stukas were quickly shot down; the remainder jettisoned their bombs and ran for home.

The next wave of bombers, approaching the coast a few minutes later, ran into the hornets' nest stirred up by the Stukas. They were Ju 88s, and they used the cloud cover to good advantage. One formation dropped their bombs on Southampton, missing the vital Spitfire production factory at Woolston but sweeping the centre of the town and the docks with a rain of high explosive and incendiary bombs, killing many civilians. Six more Ju 88s dived on the airfield at Middle Wallop, one of Fighter Command's vital sector stations. Their bombs caused only light damage, but severe damage was inflicted by another Ju 88 formation at Andover, a few miles away. Two Ju 88s were shot down by fighters.

Meanwhile, further east, over Kent, No. 11 Group was having a hard time. General Bruno Loerzer's *Fliegerkorps* II had sent in both its *Stuka-Geschwaders*, as well as a third from *Fliegerkorps* III, preceded by a swarm of Me 109s from JG 26. The Messerschmitts were able to beat off a flight of Spitfires from Kenley, allowing the eighty-six Junkers 87s to proceed unmolested to their target, the airfield of Detling near Maidstone. Fifteen minutes later the airfield lay in ruins: the hangars were burning, the operations room was wrecked, the station commander was dead and twenty British aircraft were destroyed. It was a brilliant attack, and in terms of its execution was highly successful. But there were no RAF fighters at Detling; it was a Coastal Command station.

In spite of the poor weather, the *Luftwaffe* had hurled nearly 500 bombers and 1,000 fighters into the English sky during the day. Their combat reports claimed that nine RAF airfields had been attacked, 'five with such great success that they could now be regarded as unserviceable'. Field Marshals Kesselring and Sperrle, commanding the two Air Fleets in France and the Low Countries, were well satisfied with the day's work, although it had been paid for with the loss of forty-five aircraft. It had, however, not been the decisive blow they had anticipated.

On the other side of the Channel, too, 13 August had been hailed as a success by the RAF. It was true that three airfields had been badly damaged, but not one of them was a fighter base. The RAF's loss was thirteen aircraft and seven pilots.

So, for the bomber and fighter crews of the *Luftwaffe* and the pilots of the RAF's Spitfires and Hurricanes, Eagle

Day drew to a close. But for another small group of pilots and gunners, the day was just beginning.

'We got away to a poor start yesterday,' Armstrong told the crews assembled in the briefing room that evening, 'through no fault of our own. Luckily for us, the Huns decided to leave Manston alone today. The airfield is still in a mess, but at least it's usable.' He turned to the map on the briefing room wall. It showed the dispositions of the *Luftwaffe* units in the Channel area.

'We are putting up a maximum effort tonight,' he went on, 'and here's the plan. All our assigned targets are enemy bomber airfields, or so the Intelligence people assure us.' He moved the pointer he was holding across the map as he spoke.

'Crew Six, Flight Sergeant McIver and Sergeant Smith. I'm giving you the short trip, to Lille. It won't be a piece of cake, though, so watch your step.' The freckle-faced, fair-haired McIver, a New Zealander, looked at his gunner and grinned. Both were aware that they formed the least experienced crew on the Intruder Squadron, and they were determined to do well.

'Crew Five, Flight Sergeant Winters and Sergeant Redmond. You'll be going a bit further down the road to Cambrai.' Winters nodded slowly, thinking that it would be something to tell his father when he got back. His old man had fought in the Battle of Cambrai in 1917, as part of the crew of one of the first British tanks to go into action. Redmond, his gunner, was an Irishman from

County Cork; like so many of his countrymen, he had volunteered to fight for Britain on the outbreak of war, despite the Irish Free State's neutrality.

'Crew Four, Flight Sergeant Van Berg and Sergeant Jordison your target is Evreux.' The pointer tapped a spot close to the River Seine, midway between Rouen and Paris. 'I've given you that one so you can follow the river. We all know your navigation is bloody awful.' Van Berg and Jordison both laughed. The South African was probably the best pilot-navigator on the squadron, with a homing pigeon's sense of direction. He and Jordison had a great deal in common, including a passion for rugby football, and they made a first-rate team.

'Which brings me to the hierarchy. Crew Three, Lieutenant Baird and Sergeant Copeland, will be going to Montdidier, here, south-east of Amiens. That's a tricky one for you, Dickie, because there's quite a concentration of enemy fighter airfields in the vicinity, so you'll have to worm your way past them.'

Baird took a pull on the Senior Service cigarette he was smoking and raised a quizzical eyebrow. His gunner, a small, balding individual from the Channel Islands – now occupied by the Germans – was capable of identifying any aircraft, enemy or friendly, from any angle in any kind of visual condition. Rumour had it that he used specially-tailored lavatory paper with silhouettes of aeroplanes on it, which was why he allegedly spent so long in the Sergeants' Mess 'bog' every morning. 'Crew Two, Captain

Kalinski and Sergeant Burton. Your objective is Argentan, in Normandy, south of Falaise.'

A slow, reminiscent smile spread over Kalinski's face. The Pole still wore his French Air Force uniform; the Royal Air Force had not yet seen fit to award him a commission with the equivalent rank of flight lieutenant. Argentan was in the middle of Calvados country, and Kalinski allowed his mind to dwell on the pleasures of food and drink for a moment. His gunner, already used to the pilot's drinking habits, knew exactly what he was thinking. Kalinski had little time for the class divisions between officers and airmen, and the two had made several sorties into various English hostelries since they teamed up.

'Argentan is apparently stiff with Stukas,' Armstrong informed him, 'so you could have quite a bit of fun. Now to the cream of the cream, Crew One. That's myself and Sergeant Kershaw,' he added unnecessarily. 'We'll be taking the longest trip, to Orleans.' The usually stoic Kershaw permitted himself an inward groan. My fault, he thought, for volunteering to fly with the Boss. I should have known we'd end up doing the long ones.

'We'll stagger our take-off times,' Armstrong continued, 'so that we'll all make our respective landfalls on the enemy coast at about the same time. In that way, we'll retain an element of surprise. Now, the Intelligence Officer has obligingly marked the map at the places where the coastal flak is believed to be lightest. Notice I use the word 'believed', so don't take anything for granted. We are also told that the Huns don't have any night-fighters, but that doesn't mean no fighters will be airborne. The weather all over western France will be pretty clear, so once they know we're there it's quite probable they'll launch day-fighters to look for us.'

He turned to face them squarely, planting the long pointer – it was actually a snooker cue – between his feet.

'One important point, and I want it to sink in. No heroics. Don't waste time and effort stoogeing around in the target area, looking for trouble. Remember that we are all new to this game. Identify your targets, get in, give 'em a good pasting and get out. If you run into any enemy aircraft en route to and from the target, by all means have a go at them, but remember that airfield attack is your primary mission. We want to do as much damage as possible, and make the bastards sit up. And for God's sake watch out for friendly aircraft. Bomber Command Blenheims will be attacking the seaplane base at Brest and a sizeable force of Whitleys is being sent out to attack Milan and Turin. It's just possible that we may see some of them, so don't forget that a Whitley can look very much like a Dornier from some angles. The poor beggars have a hard enough job on their hands, so we don't want any stupid accidents. Don't forget, too, that a Blenheim is easily mistaken for a Ju 88, so if you do spot a Whitley, stay well clear of it. Their gunners will have itchy trigger fingers.'

He looked towards the back of the room, where four more men sat, looking thoroughly dejected. They were the two reserve crews, bitterly disappointed at not having been selected to take part, even though they knew that a shortage of aircraft was the only reason.

Armstrong concluded the briefing with details of radio frequencies, take-off times and so on, including the appropriate recognition flares to be fired as they approached the English coast at the end of their night's work and the designated corridors in the coastal anti-aircraft cordon by which they would make their landfall. There was little to do now but take a pre-flight meal – no one felt really hungry, but they all knew they would be by the time they were well into the sortie – and wait.

Kalinski, with the longest over-water crossing ahead of him, was the first to take off, followed by Van Berg and then Armstrong at carefully calculated intervals. The other three crews, with much the same distances to fly across the narrower part of the Channel, left Manston considerably later, their aircraft roaring into the darkness with little spacing between them.

It was a few minutes before midnight when Armstrong took off, turning south as soon as the Blenheim crossed the English coast. He climbed steadily to 15,000 feet in a clear, moonless sky; it would be another couple of days before the slim crescent of the new moon showed itself. Yet the summer night was not dark, and he could see deep into France as he cruised high over the Channel.

Boulogne slid by, away to the left, and a few minutes later Le Touquet.

'About twenty miles to run until we turn inland, Kersh,' he told his gunner.

'Okay, skipper. There's a searchlight at ten o'clock.'

'I've got it.' A slim finger of light stabbed vertically into the sky several miles off their nose, wavering from side to side. 'That'll be Berck-Plage. Their sound locators will have picked us up.'

The searchlight gradually fell astern, then abruptly flicked out. Armstrong peered ahead towards the spot where the coastline swept south-westward, its outline broken by the broad expanse of the Somme estuary.

'Stand by. We're going down.' Armstrong put the Blenheim into a gradual descent, levelling out at 2,000 feet, crossing the estuary and heading inland to the west of Abbeville. This was the first real danger point of the mission, for Abbeville was one of the principal enemy fighter airfields. For the next few miles Armstrong was keyed up, ready to go down to treetop level and make a high-speed dash if Kershaw sighted any German aircraft, but the intercom remained silent. There were no fighters and, so far, no flak.

Everything depended now on accurate navigation. Armstrong had memorised every detail of his route, and checked off the landmarks as they appeared under the Blenheim's nose. They crossed the Abeville – Neufchatel road, and ten miles further on the one that ran across country from Amiens to Le Havre, on the coast. The countryside below them now was a vista of rolling, wooded hills, rising in places to 1,000 feet.

'Lights at eleven o'clock,' Kershaw reported. 'About twenty miles, I'd say.'

'That's Paris. The blackout is bloody awful.' A sprinkle of lights, pinpricks in the darkness, appeared to the south-east. Armstrong wondered briefly if the poor blackout was accidental, or whether patriotic French citizens were deliberately exposing lights, placing themselves in great danger in the process, to provide beacons for RAF bombers.

The lights drifted slowly by on the horizon. Another very definite landmark came up ahead: the River Seine. The Blenheim actually flew over it three times, for at this point the river wound and twisted and curved back on itself in the shape of a huge letter S, with the town of Mantes-la-Jolie just touching the lower curve. Armstrong increased speed a little and went down to 1,500 feet as the aircraft roared across the rooftops, then Mantes was behind him.

'I can see some flashes over to starboard, skipper,' Kershaw said urgently. 'Doesn't look like flak, though. Whoops! I spoke too soon. There's flak all right, and lots of it.'

Armstrong looked. A long way off, a small area of sky twinkled with red pinpoints. There was a fitful reddish glow at their base. Both Armstrong and Kershaw knew that they were seeing Van Berg's attack going in at Evreux, right on schedule. The Huns would be wide awake now; it looked as if something were well ablaze over there, and he hoped fervently that it was not the South African's Blenheim.

Still further away to the west, beyond the range of their vision, Kalinski should be about to start his attack on Argentan. The Germans would be wide awake now, all right, thought Armstrong, as he checked the distance they had to run to the target. Eighty miles; another half-hour, at the progress they were making. An unexpectedly stiff breeze had sprung up from the south and they were flying directly into it, cutting down their ground speed to 160 knots. Armstrong consoled himself with the thought that unless the wind veered, it would help them on the way out.

They passed over a cluster of roads and railway lines that came to a confluence in Chartres, then picked up another railroad that ran almost due south, over on the right. It led directly to Orleans and Armstrong followed it, keeping it constantly in sight off the Blenheim's wingtip. He felt the adrenalin rising as the town made famous by Joan of Arc came into view, a sprawling dark patch under the stars. No lights were visible here, and there was nothing to guide him as he searched for the aerodrome, which lay about three miles to the north-west of the town. He could see the River Loire, though, running in a great east-west curve through Orleans, and realised with a sudden shock that he must have overflown the airfield, or very nearly.

He turned and went up to 3,000 feet, flying directly over the middle of Orleans and retracing his course, heading north-north-west. Suddenly, almost directly ahead and only two miles away, twin rows of dim blue lights popped into life, forming a road in the darkness. An instant later he saw a dark shadow flit across them, and he realised that he was looking at an aircraft making its approach to land. He throttled back instinctively, desperately trying not to overshoot. The dark shadow had now sprouted red and green navigation lights at its wingtips, and was descending rapidly.

He followed it as it flew downwind, closing in gradually. The fact that the flarepath had not been switched on until the last moment indicated that the enemy knew that an intruder was in the vicinity; either that, or they had been alerted by the Whitley bombers, passing high over France en route to their targets in Italy.

The enemy aircraft began its turn across wind and Armstrong followed suit. The range was down to a hundred yards now, and the black bulk filled his gunsight. He took a deep breath and opened fire.

The Blenheim shuddered to the recoil of its machine guns and four streams of tracer lanced out from beneath its belly. Smoke from the gun pack, reeking of cordite, invaded the cockpit. Ahead, orange flashes danced and sparkled all over the target and a long tongue of flame erupted almost immediately from a fuel tank in its port wing, illuminating a square-cut, corrugated fuselage and the white-edged black cross stamped on it. Armstrong at once identified the aircraft as a Junkers Ju 52 three-engined transport.

He gave it another burst of fire and then turned away sharply as it reared up suddenly in front of him, showering sparks and glowing debris. Then its nose dropped sharply and it plummeted straight into the ground right on the end of the flarepath, which was abruptly extinguished.

Armstrong turned steeply in the opposite direction, lining up with the aerodrome. He raced low over the blazing wreck of the Ju 52, its light throwing hangars and other buildings into sharp relief. Several aircraft – they appeared to be Junkers 88s, but there was no time to identify them precisely – were parked in a line close to one of the hangars and Armstrong made for them, thundering along only feet above the ground. A red sleet of tracer converged on the speeding Blenheim from all angles, but his extremely low altitude must have confused the gunners, because the fire passed harmlessly overhead.

He held his thumb down on the firing button in a long, continuous burst as he passed over the line of enemy bombers. Behind him, Kershaw raked them in turn as they came into his field of vision, swivelling his turret and continuing to fire while his targets were still within range.

Armstrong kept the Blenheim down low until he was

well clear of the aerodrome, then pulled the fighter up in a steep ascending turn, climbing to 5,000 feet and pointing its nose towards the north. Looking over to his right, he could clearly see the funeral pyre of the Ju 52, and there were other fires too, among the bombers he had attacked. With no intention of lingering in the area, he pushed the nose down again and descended to 1,500 feet. As they sped away, Kershaw reported that the enemy anti-aircraft gunners were still blazing away into an empty sky.

The flight back across France was uneventful, although they had to run the gauntlet of searchlights and flak as they crossed the coast. One shell exploded perilously close, its splinters rattling like hail on the Blenheim's wings and fuselage; luckily, the shrapnel was practically spent, and apart from peppering the paintwork it caused no damage.

They landed back at Manston just after 03.30, their homeward progress, as Armstrong had predicted, having been helped by the tail wind. To his great joy, Armstrong found that the others were all back safely, and that all had enjoyed a measure of success. The youthful McIver and Smith, his gunner, were the heroes of the hour; they had caught two fat Heinkels in the circuit at Lille and destroyed both of them. At Evreux, Van Berg and Jordison had caused some havoc among the Ju 88s of KG 54; the South African reported that he had found a hangar with its doors open and had fired a long burst into it, his incendiary bullets setting fire to some aircraft inside.

Winters and Redmond, prowling around the clutch of

airfields near Cambrai – where the Dornier 17s of KG 2 were based – had found no aircraft to attack, either in the air or on the ground, but they had shot up an enemy convoy, heading for one of the aerodromes with masked headlights, and thought they had hit a pair of petrol bowsers; at any rate, they had left a couple of very satis-fying fires behind them.

Baird and Copeland had enjoyed an amazing stroke of luck. They had found no worthwhile targets at all, either in the air or on the ground, and had been on their way home, their ammunition boxes still full, when they had almost collided with an aircraft flying low over the Channel and heading north. Closer inspection had revealed it to be a Heinkel 115 floatplane, doubtless heading towards the Thames estuary on a minelaying mission. After trading shots with it for a couple of minutes they had sent it down into the water in mid-Channel and had alerted the air-sea rescue service; they were waiting to hear whether the German crew had been picked up. It wasn't that they were particularly interested in the welfare of the Germans; it was just that they were keen to acquire souvenirs.

That left Kalinski and Burton, whose attack on Argentan, as the combat report later stated, had been 'prosecuted with great vigour'. Kalinski, with a typical Polish disregard for self-preservation, had made several runs over the target, strafing everything in sight. He and his gunner both agreed that they had knocked out a group of five Stukas, clustered together in a corner of the aerodrome. Kalinski was the only one of them to have used flares in his attack, which had illuminated the target nicely but which had also illuminated his Blenheim. It had collected a great many bullet and shrapnel holes, but nothing vital had been hit and it was airworthy enough to fly back to Bircham Newton, where it could be patched up.

All in all, it had been a promising start. But Armstrong knew that they had been lucky. He was under no illusion about what the future might have in store.

The daylight hours of Wednesday, 14 August brought cloud and rain. It persisted throughout the morning, giving Armstrong and his tired crews the chance of a few hours' sleep uninterrupted by the crump of bombs and the roar of aero-engines. At 11.30, as the weather began to clear, the Blenheims took off again and headed north for Bircham Newton. They were only just in time. Exactly forty minutes later, the Me 110s of Special Group 210 again made a surprise attack on Manston, their bombs blasting four hangars and several dispersals – including the one recently vacated by the Intruder Squadron – into ruin. But Manston's gunners had the last word, scattering the wreckage of two 110s across the airfield.

# Chapter Eight

*Black Thursday: 15 August 1940*

Low cloud dominated the scene at daybreak on 15 August, and the Luftwaffe's meteorologists predicted that it would persist throughout the day. It seemed a good opportunity for Hermann Goering to call a conference, and early that morning the commanders of Air Fleets 2 and 3, Field Marshals Kesselring – known throughout the German Air Force as 'Smiling Albert' – and Hugo Sperrle, who wore a perpetual scowl on his face, were summoned to Karinhall, the C-in-C's HQ and magnificent country mansion near Berlin. With them went their immediate subordinates, including Bruno Loerzer, commanding Fliegerkorps II, and Wolfram Baron von Richthofen, nephew of the famous fighter ace of the Great War, a mercurial little major-general whose Stuka dive bombers had played such a significant part in the Battle of France.

The meteorologists, as it turned out, were wrong. Shortly after ten o'clock the weather began to clear, and an hour later the clouds had broken up completely.

In the operations room of *Fliegerkorps* II, just south of Calais, *Oberst* Paul Deichmann, the senior staff officer on duty, found himself in a dilemma. Bruno Loerzer was absent, but with the Air Corps squadrons standing ready to go and the weather improving all the time, the opportunity was too good to miss. Taking the initiative, Deichmann ordered II Air Corps' two Stuka groups, *Hauptmann* Keil's II/St-G 1, and IV (St)-LG 1, under *Hauptmann* von Brauchitsch, to take off for their targets in southern England. Then Deichmann drove at top speed to Cap Blanc Nez, where the advanced HQ of Air Fleet 2 was situated in an underground bunker. The operations officer there, *Oberstleutnant* Rieckhoff, waved a sheet of paper under Deichmann's nose. It was a signal from Berlin, forbidding any attack to be carried out that day. But it was too late; the Stuka squadrons were already droning towards the English coast.

At Gravesend, the pilots of No. 501 Squadron, veterans of the campaign in France, were on readiness beside their Hurricanes when the alarm went up at 11.29. Within minutes the Hurricanes were climbing hard over the coast between Dover and Dungeness to intercept the first wave of enemy aircraft: forty Stukas, escorted by about as many Messerschmitt 109s. Also heading for the enemy formation were the Spitfires of No. 54 Squadron, which had been scrambled from Hornchurch.

The bombers were met by the two fighter squadrons as they crossed the coast, but the British pilots soon found themselves engaged in savage dogfights with the 109s and could do little to frustrate the attacks. In perfect echelon formation the Stukas swept down on the airfield at Lympne and peeled off one by one, letting fly with their 250-kg bombs. Then they droned away, leaving Lympne so hard hit that it was out of action for two days.

The Ju 87s and their escorts flew away across the Channel; the Spitfires and Hurricanes returned to their bases, to refuel and rearm in readiness for the next assault. When it came, it was from an unexpected quarter.

So far, the attacks by *Luftflotten 2* and 3 had been hurled against southern England, where the airfields of Fighter Command's No. 11 Group stretched like a defensive shield on the approaches to London, north and south of the Thames, and the squadrons of No. 10 Group had the task of defending the seaports of the south-west. Further north, from East Anglia to the River Humber, No. 12 Group stood ready to come to the assistance of the southern squadrons, but so far had not been seriously committed to the battle; while further north still, the area of No. 13 Group, extending from Yorkshire into Scotland, was believed to be relatively safe from heavy attack. It was here, under Dowding's policy, that the battle-weary squadrons from the south were sent to rest and re-equip on a rotation basis.

Four hundred miles from the quiet aerodromes of 13

Group, at Stavanger in Norway and Aalborg in Denmark, the squadrons of General Hans-Jurgen Stumpff's *Luftflotte* 5 – the smallest of the three Air Fleets confronting the British Isles – had been waiting to play their part in the great air offensive against England. Now, at eleven o'clock on this Thursday morning, they were given their chance. Over Stavanger, the sky was black with aircraft as sixty-three Heinkel He 111 bombers of KG 26 formed up and set course over the North Sea, accompanied by twenty-one Messerschmitt 110s of ZG 76, the *Luftwaffe's* most experienced twin-engined fighter unit. Its crews had seen action in Poland; they had been responsible for the air defence of the big German naval base at Wilhelmshaven during the winter of 1939-40, during which time they had inflicted severe losses on RAF bombers attempting to raid northern Germany in daylight; they had been the first German fighter unit to land in Norway at the start of the German invasion; and finally, they had fought with distinction in the Battle of France, carrying out escort duties.

Today's mission was the longest ZG 76 had been called upon to fly so far. The bombers' targets were the airfields in northeast England, and – taking into account the distance that would have to be flown over enemy territory – the Heinkels and their escorts would have to make a round trip of anything up to 1,200 miles. To give the Messerschmitts the necessary range, each aircraft was fitted with a 220-gallon auxiliary fuel tank mounted under the fuselage.

Although events in the south had already shown that

the Me 110 was a far from ideal escort fighter, inferior in performance to both the Spitfire and Hurricane, the Germans did not expect serious trouble. According to *Luftwaffe* Intelligence, most of the fighter squadrons of No. 13 Group had been transferred south, to counter the heavy air attacks in No. 11 Group's area.

Intelligence, however, was wrong, as the Germans were soon to discover to their cost. Unknown to them, five squadrons of Spitfires and Hurricanes lay in their path. And with only marginal reserves of fuel, the Messerschmitts would be unable to engage in prolonged air combat.

Just before one o'clock, radar stations on the north-east coast of England picked up a large trace, believed to be hostile, about a hundred miles out to sea. The radar plot suggested that the enemy aircraft were heading towards the Firth of Forth, following a south-westerly track.

In Northumberland, the rooftops of the little village of Acklington trembled to the roar of Rolls-Royce Merlins as the twelve Spitfires of No. 72 Squadron took off from their nearby RAF base, climbing flat out towards the coast in response to the radar's warning. All the while, the fighter controller transmitted the latest details to the Spitfire leader, Flight Lieutenant Ted Graham. Thirty-plus bogeys, heading two-zero-zero degrees . . . altitude five-thousand-plus feet.

In fact, the radar was plotting a formation of twenty Heinkel 115 seaplanes, which had been sent out by *Luftflotte* 5 to create a diversion. The main force of bombers and fighters was to have crossed the English coast a good hundred miles further south, within striking distance of its airfield targets in Yorkshire. The ruse might have worked – had it not been for the German practice of relying on one master navigator in the leading bomber of the formation. The rest of the bombers simply followed his directions, and in this case the directions were faulty. The Heinkels and their escorts were heading for a point on the Northumberland coast seventy miles north of their intended landfall. No one would ever know what had gone wrong, because in just a few more minutes the navigator and the rest of his crew would be dead.

Ted Graham's Spitfires climbed hard over the Fame Islands, the pilots searching the sky ahead for a first sign of the thirty or so enemy aircraft they were expecting. Instead, they saw a cloud of black dots, growing steadily larger as the two formations closed. Taken aback, it took Graham a few seconds to find his voice. Then he quickly ordered the squadron into a wide, climbing turn, positioning the Spitfires for an attack out of the sun.

The Heinkels were flying at 8,000 feet, with the Messerschmitts 2-3,000 feet higher. The Spitfires' attack took the Germans completely by surprise; they had not expected to encounter British fighters so soon, if at all. The first to spot the danger was *Feldwebel* Richter, bringing up the rear of the Me 110 formation. He yelled a warning over the radio and pulled his fighter round to meet the oncoming Spitfires.

Richter's warning came too late to save the leader of the Me 110 formation, *Hauptmann* Restemeyer. In the fighter's rear cockpit, in place of the usual gunner, sat *Hauptmann* Hartwig, the head of X Air Corps' radio monitoring section. His job was to listen to the British fighter frequencies and gather Intelligence on squadron movements. Unfortunately, he had not been monitoring the frequency used by 72 Squadron.

A Spitfire flashed through the Me 110 formation, grey smoke trails from its eight machine-guns converging on Restemeyer's 110. There was a sudden, blinding flash as bullets ripped into the fighter's auxiliary fuel tank, full of highly explosive petrol vapour. The 110 was instantly transformed into a fiery ball, rolling over and over towards the sea. Neither Restemeyer nor Hartwig had stood a chance of getting out.

*Feldwebel* Richter, meanwhile, had found himself in serious trouble. A Spitfire came curving towards him out of the sun, flashes twinkling along the leading edges of its wings. There were a couple of loud bangs, and Richter was dimly aware of his cockpit canopy flying to pieces. Then he blacked out, his weight slumping forward over the stick. The Messerschmitt nosed over and dived steeply towards the sea. In the rear cockpit the gunner, *Unteroffizier* Geischecker, jettisoned his escape panel and baled out, thinking that the pilot was dead.

Richter woke up to find an icy blast of air screaming through the cockpit and the sea whirling up to meet him.

Summoning all his strength, he managed to pull the 110 out of its headlong dive. Bleeding profusely from a scalp wound, he turned and headed for home across the North Sea, keeping just below a layer of broken cloud. Miraculously, he made it. A couple of hours later, utterly exhausted and in considerable pain, he made a forced landing near Esbjerg. Geischecker was never seen again.

Ted Graham's fighters had now been joined by the Hurricanes of No. 79 Squadron, also from Acklington. They swept in from all sides, hammering at the wilting Me 110 formation.

The commander of ZG 76's No. 2 Flight, *Leutnant* Uellenbeck, went into a steep turn to starboard and managed to get on the tail of a Spitfire. He opened fire and the British fighter broke away sharply and went down in a shallow dive, trailing a thin streamer of smoke, to disappear in the cloud layer. An instant later Uellenbeck was attacked in turn by another Spitfire. He twisted and turned, desperately trying to shake off the dogged fighter as bullets thudded into his 110. His wingman, *Feldwebel* Schumacher, came to the rescue just in time, driving off the Spitfire with a few well-aimed bursts. Things were getting too hot for comfort. Uellenbeck pressed the R/T button, ordering his fighters to drop their auxiliary tanks and form a defensive circle. By this method, each 110 could cover the tail of the one in front. It was their only hope of survival.

Further ahead, No. 3 Flight under *Leutnant* Gordon

Gollob was still keeping close escort with a squadron of Heinkels, despite determined fighter attacks. One of the pilots, *Feldwebel* Linke, went after a Spitfire which had just shot one of the bombers down in flames, overhauling the British fighter as it climbed away. He fired a long burst from a range of less than a hundred yards; the Spitfire faltered and dropped away in a tight spiral, but Linke had no chance to see what became of it because at that moment two more Spitfires dived on him. Bullets ripped into the Messerschmitt's port wing, putting one engine out of action. Linke dropped into the clouds with the two fighters in hot pursuit. Altering course to throw off his attackers, he broke through the cloud base at 2,500 feet and turned for home. A few seconds later he saw, in the distance, two aircraft fall through the cloud layer and plunge burning into the sea. On reaching Jever a couple of hours later, after a nerve-racking single-engined flight low over the water, Linke reported that the aircraft he had seen crashing were Spitfires. In fact, they were Me 110s . . .

Another Messerschmitt, harried by Hurricanes, inexplicably turned south-west and flew deep into the moors of County Durham's Teesdale. The Hurricanes shot it down near the old market town of Barnard Castle. The crew, *Oberleutnant* Kettling and *Obergefreiter* Volk, survived the experience and were taken prisoner.

Meanwhile, deprived of most of their fighter escort, the Heinkels were droning southwards along the coast, searching for their targets. As they approached the River Tyne and the sprawling city of Newcastle, they were subjected to a fresh onslaught by British fighters – this time the Hurricanes of No. 605 Squadron, on patrol from Drem in southern Scotland. 'B' Flight, led by Flight Lieutenant Archie McKellar, was the first to make contact with the enemy. McKellar ordered his pilots into line astern and told them to follow him into the sun. Then he led them in a diving attack on the rear aircraft of the leading group.

Lining up on a Heinkel, he opened fire from 250 yards. After one three-second burst the bomber fell away in a spiral dive and McKellar was forced to break away sharply as he came under fire from a pair of Heinkels behind him. The bombers were by now over Newcastle and McKellar ordered his pilots to make individual attacks, forcing the Heinkels to take evasive action and preventing them from dropping their bombs accurately.

Some of the bombers jettisoned their loads over the Tyne shipyards and veered away out to sea. The remainder flew on towards Sunderland, still harried by 605 Squadron. Archie McKellar attacked another Heinkel, which took violent evasive action and got away, then he selected the leading bomber in the formation and swept down in a beam attack, giving the aircraft a long eight-second burst. It started to go down, with both engines pouring smoke. McKellar turned steeply and fired at a Heinkel which flashed across his nose; that, too, began to burn. Looking round, he picked up a straggler and closed in astern, firing off the remainder of his ammunition. He saw the bomber's rear gunner throw up his hands and suddenly disappear beneath his cupola; an instant later the Heinkel's starboard engine began to trail grey smoke. Then, low on fuel and with his ammunition exhausted, McKellar left the bomber to its uncertain fate and headed for the nearest airfield.

During their engagement over the Tyne, the pilots of 605 Squadron destroyed four enemy aircraft and damaged several more. The remainder, under attack now by the Spitfires of No. 41 Squadron from Catterick and the Hurricanes of No. 607 from Usworth, near Sunderland, unloaded their bombs more or less at random and made their escape as quickly as possible. Behind them, scattered along the coast or inland, they left the wrecks of eight Heinkels and seven Me 110s. It was a high price to pay for failure.

At Bircham Newton, within the boundary of Air Vice-Marshal Trafford Leigh-Mallory's No. 12 Group, the crews of the two Blenheim squadrons were just finishing off their lunch when an urgent call came over the tannoy, ordering every fighter that was armed and fuelled to get airborne. Armstrong and his fellow officers raced down to the dispersal to find most of the other crews already there – two had been at readiness – and the ground crews standing by to help start up. Briggs, the adjutant, was looking worried.

'What's to do, Briggsie?' Armstrong queried, pulling on his Mae West lifejacket.

'There's a big air battle going on up north, sir,' Briggs

told him, 'and now radar has picked up what appears to be another large incoming hostile formation, on a direct course for Flamborough Head. Sector Control wants every available aircraft off the ground.'

His words were momentarily drowned by a crescendo of sound as the Blenheims of 235 Squadron roared into the air, heading toward the coast. Armstrong ran towards his aircraft; Kershaw was already settling into his gun turret. A few minutes later all six of the Intruder Squadron's Blenheims were also airborne, and heading in the same direction. Armstrong tuned the radio to the frequency of the sector control station at Duxford and asked for instructions.

'Fifty-plus bogeys, angels one-six, eight-oh miles north of you. Patrol Flamborough Head area,' the controller told him.

Eighty miles, and due north: that meant the enemy formation was very close to the Yorkshire coast. Armstrong knew that his ponderous Blenheims had no chance of getting there before the enemy made landfall, and so did the controller. The best they could hope for was to catch the bombers as they ran for home.

A few moments later, an excited voice broke in on the frequency. 'Radpoe Leader calling. Fifty-plus bandits, heading for the coast, range ten miles, angels one-five. Tally ho!'

'Radpoe' was the callsign of No. 616 Squadron, the 'South Yorkshire' squadron of the Auxiliary Air Force, whose Spitfires had been scrambled from Leconfield a little earlier. Their pilots were now seeing, in the distance, the fifty aircraft that formed the second prong of *Luftflotte* 5's attack: not Heinkels this time, but the fast Junkers 88 dive-bombers of KG 30, the Denmark-based *Geschwader* from Aalborg.

The Spitfires swept headlong towards the enemy formation and began their attack. They were followed by half a dozen Hurricanes of 'A' Flight No. 73 Squadron, based at Church Fenton, which had been patrolling over a convoy off Hornsea when they were suddenly given a 'vector' that brought them into contact with the bombers. In the running fight that followed seven bombers were shot down, but the remainder split up into eight groups and pressed on with determination to their target, the bomber aerodrome of Driffield. Their bombs destroyed four hangars and other buildings, wrecking twelve Whitley bombers and killing thirteen RAF personnel; the whole airfield was pock-marked with craters, and it would be the end of the year before it was operational again.

Armstrong and his pilots, and those of 235 Squadron some distance ahead, could do nothing other than listen to the jubilant cries of the fighter pilots as they ravaged the Ju 88 formation. By the time they reached their patrol area the surviving Junkers were already speeding away to the north-east, and although they gave chase they had no hope of catching the much faster enemy bombers. A few minutes later, sector control ordered them back to base.

At 15.00, while the Ju 88s were heading back to Aalborg, the RAF fighter squadrons in the South were once more gearing up to meet a fresh onslaught. Radar had detected a big raid assembling over the Belgian coast. It was the Dornier 17s of KG 3, led by *Oberst* von Chamier-Glisczinski, and this time the Germans were taking no chances. Escorting the sixty or so bombers were the Me 109s of four fighter *Geschwaders*, and they were the best the *Luftwaffe* could put into the air. Many of the pilots had begun their combat careers during the Spanish Civil War; they included Major Adolf Galland, leading a squadron of JG 26.

While the radar's probing beams kept watch on the enemy formations building up over Belgium, another force of attackers roared low over the Channel, flying almost at wave top height to escape detection. They were the twenty-four Messerschmitt 110s of Rubensdorffer's Special Group 210, unescorted this time by Lehmann's 109s. With the RAF's fighter controllers confused by plots of raids coming in from all around the clock, and with eleven Spitfire and Hurricane squadrons already airborne to meet them, SG 210's low-level strike once again took the defences by surprise. The Messerschmitts raced across the coast and bombed the airfield of Martlesham Heath, home base of No. 17 (Hurricane) Squadron. One swift bombing run was all that was needed; the Hurricanes returned to Martlesham to find the airfield in ruins, with hangars and buildings in flames and the surface pitted with bomb craters.

Meanwhile, the Dorniers of KG 3 were droning steadily towards the coast, with the squadrons of Messerschmitts weaving overhead and on their flanks. Over Kent, one group broke away and bombed the airfield at Eastchurch, while the other two groups flew on to attack Rochester aerodrome, their bombs exploding on the taxiways and hangars and among parked aircraft. A shower of bombs went down on an aircraft factory on the northern edge of the field, followed by incendiary and delayed action bombs dropped by the last wave. It was the factory that built the huge Short Stirling four-engined bomber, and the attack set back production by several weeks.

In mid-afternoon there was a two-hour lull, during which sweating ground crews patched up minor battle damage and the pilots snatched a hasty sandwich and mug of tea while their fighters were being refuelled and rearmed. Then, shortly before five o'clock, another series of radar plots began building up over the Cherbourg peninsula.

This time, the threat came from General Sperrle's *Luftflotte* 3. The attack was led by four groups of Ju 88s belonging to LG 1 from Orleans, the scene of Armstrong's intruder raid of a couple of nights before, followed by two groups of Stukas from the Cherbourg-based St-G 1, all under a formidable fighter umbrella of Me 109s and 110s. At 18.00 the 200-strong armada launched itself across the Channel towards the Isle of Wight.

Thanks to the two-hour respite, the RAF was ready.

Fierce air battles blazed up all over the south coast as, one after the other, fourteen squadrons of Spitfires and Hurricanes – about 170 aircraft – engaged the enemy. The Messerschmitt groups now found themselves fighting hard for their own survival and the bombers, left to their fate, suffered heavy losses as they battled their way inland. The Stuka formations were quickly shattered, and few succeeded in breaking through to their targets. The four Ju 88 groups of LG 1 were only a little luckier: the rearmost group of seven aircraft, continually harried by Spitfires, was shot to pieces, only two crews returning to base, and only the leading group managed to bomb the sector airfield of Middle Wallop. The other two groups, chased by the Spitfires of No. 609 Squadron and the Hurricanes of No. 32, jettisoned their bombs and headed for the coast at top speed.

At 19.35 the Hurricanes of No. 32 Squadron were once again airborne from Biggin Hill after a very fast turn-round, and were patrolling Dover at 10,000 feet under Squadron Leader Mike Crossley when they were told that an enemy raid was heading towards Croydon, on the outskirts of London. Crossley immediately turned his formation back towards the capital, searching for the enemy.

The enemy, in fact, was Special Group 210 again, whose fifteen bomb-carrying Me 110s and the eight 109s of the close escort were at that moment crossing the English coast. High above, their wings glinting golden in the evening sunshine, weaved their top fighter cover, drawn from the Messerschmitt 109s of JG 52.

Special Group 210's target was Kenley, the vital sector station to the south of London. At the same time, a Dornier 17 Group was on its way to attack the equally important base of Biggin Hill.

Leading SG 210, *Hauptmann* Walter Rubensdorffer picked out an airfield which he identified as Kenley. At that moment, there was a warning shout over the radio as someone in Lehmann's flight spotted No. 32's Hurricanes, diving hard from astern just too late to break up the German's attack. The bombs whistled down, exploding among the hangars and destroying no fewer than forty aircraft. But the aircraft were trainers, and the airfield was not Kenley, but Croydon. As it turned out, the Dorniers had made a similar mistake, bombing West Malling instead of Biggin Hill.

As Rubensdorffer's Messerschmitts climbed away after their attack, Mike Crossley's Hurricanes fell on them. Crossley fired a long burst and a 110 streamed flames, diving into the ground and exploding. Crossley went after a second 110 and raked its port wing, putting an engine out of action. A yellow parachute blossomed out behind the enemy aircraft and the man beneath it – *Leutnant* Ortner – watched helplessly as the 110's nose dropped until it was in a near-vertical dive. It crashed in a sheet of blazing fuel, taking Ortner's gunner, *Obergefreiter* Lohmann, to his death.

Crossley's fighters were now joined by the Hurricanes of No. 111 Squadron, which had been on their way back to their base at Croydon when the 110s bombed it. 'Treble One' Squadron's commander, Squadron Leader John Thompson, caught the last 110 as it was coming out of its dive, fired, and saw chunks of metal fly off the German's starboard wing and engine. The 110 crash-landed in a field, and the pilot and observer were taken prisoners.

Meanwhile, the other 110s were corkscrewing up in a defensive circle, gaining height and waiting for an opportunity to make a break for it. Suddenly, Lehmann's fighter flight dived slap through the middle of the fray, momentarily scattering the Hurricanes before climbing hard to join the defensive circle. With the Me 109s now fighting a rearguard action, Rubensdorffer saw his chance and broke away with four Me 110s, heading south-west for the Channel coast at Eastbourne. They were soon lost to sight in the haze.

The Spitfires of No. 64 Squadron were returning home to their base at Kenley after a patrol over Lympne when the Kenley controller came on the air and vectored them on to the fleeing 110s. They caught the Germans just short of the coast and came at them from the beam, out of the sinking sun. There was a sword-thrust of tracer, a flicker of flame and Rubensdorffer's 110 turned slowly over on its back. Leaving a trail of thickening smoke it hit the ground at Bletchinglye Farm, Rotherfield, and disintegrated in a cloud of blazing wreckage. Neither

Rubensdorffer nor his gunner, *Obergefreiter* Kretzer, had baled out.

Frantically, Rubensdorffer's wingman, *Oberleutnant* Habisch, broke hard left and took evasive action, twisting and turning across the Sussex countryside. He was too late. He and his gunner, *Unteroffizier* Elfner, baled out moments before their burning aircraft hit the ground near Hawkhurst and blew up. The other 110s dived away over the coast, throttles wide open, and disappeared towards France.

Back at Calais-Marck, the survivors of Special Group 210 counted the cost of the raid. Thirteen faces were missing: the crews of six Me 110s and *Leutnant* Marx, Lehmann's deputy flight commander. Lehmann had seen Marx bale out, and assumed that he was safe; he was a talented pilot, and his loss would be keenly felt.

Similar losses were being keenly felt all over north-west France and the Low Countries. Between dawn and dusk on what was already being called *Schwarzer Donnerstag* – Black Thursday – the *Luftwaffe* had lost seventy-five aircraft. It was the biggest blow the Germans would ever take in British skies, and not only in the material sense. For the first time, the *Luftwaffe*, cocksure after a year of almost unchecked victory, had taken a bloody nose. RAF Fighter Command, Hermann Goering claimed, was finished; but his airmen knew otherwise.

# Chapter Nine

Dickie Baird gave a sudden hoot of laughter and passed the copy of the Daily Mirror to Armstrong. Both men were sitting in the ante-room of the Officers' Mess at Bircham Newton. It was teatime. The date on the newspaper was Friday, 16 August 1940.

'Take a look at that,' Baird said. 'There, down at the bottom, in the middle.'

Armstrong looked, and chuckled. 'PLANE TRAP IS SECRET', said the headline. 'A plane trap erected by the Ministry of Transport caught a German bomber yesterday and wrecked it. All the crew were killed. British military authorities have no intention of giving away to the enemy details of the plane trap. The trap is the latest 'hush-hush' defence weapon, as the Nazis have already learned to their cost. More news of its formidable and effective nature can be expected soon.'

'Good God, whatever next?' Armstrong muttered through his mirth. 'That's about as believable as this is.' His fingertip tapped the main headline, which shrilled to the world at large that the RAF had shot down 144 German aeroplanes during the big raids of the previous day. He offered the paper back to Baird, who shook his head.

'No, you can have it. I'm for another cuppa.' The Fleet Air Arm pilot got up, made his way to the long table that stood near the ante-room door and came back with a cup of tea in one hand and a plate of bread and jam in the other, carefully subsiding into his armchair with a sigh of contentment. Armstrong, meanwhile, read on in silence. An account of yesterday's raid on Croydon captured his attention.

*Fourteen dive-bombers, protected by fighters, attacked Croydon Aerodrome. High explosive 'screamers' and incendiary bombs were dropped. Some people were killed and a number injured.*

*Raiders were first seen when they started to dive about three miles from the aerodrome. People in the streets saw them come to a few hundred feet before the bombs were released . . .*

There was a picture of what was left of an Me 110 on page three, lying in the road in front of some Croydon houses it had demolished as it came down. There were also some snippets of personal experience from the good folk of Croydon whose daily routine had been rudely shattered.

'Can't see anything about the northern raids,' Armstrong commented, flicking through the pages.

'Back page,' Baird told him through a mouthful of bread and jam. 'In the middle column.'

Armstrong looked. There was not much; just a few brief paragraphs. They told Armstrong that a man called Levi Wharton, twenty-four, a farm hand, had been hedge clipping in a field when he had been killed by a bomb; the lone raider had then circled a seaside town and dropped four bombs before turning its machine-guns on two children. They were killed and a workman was taken to hospital with a fractured leg. The newspaper repeated part of an official communique:

*Enemy aircraft again appeared in large numbers off our coasts today. During the morning a large force of bombers unsuccessfully attacked several RAF aerodromes in the south-east. Our fighters engaged the enemy and inflicted heavy casualties.*

*Early in the afternoon a number of enemy aircraft crossed the north-east coast. Bombs were dropped on the Tyneside area and in a residential district of Sunderland. Further inland bombs were dropped at several isolated points. At an RAF aerodrome some damage was done to buildings causing a number of casualties.*

And that was all there was to record one of Fighter Command's biggest successes of the day. Armstrong tossed the paper aside in disgust.

'Bloody typical,' he muttered. 'Anything happens north of the Watford Gap, and nobody wants to know about it.'

The Watford Gap was the name of a celebrated petrol station, made famous by commercial travellers who claimed that it marked the dividing line between North and South.

After the hectic events of yesterday, Friday had been a quiet day in the North, although the *Luftwaffe* had continued its airfield attacks during the morning, striking in force at Brize Norton, Manston, West Malling, Tangmere, Gosport, Lee-on-Solent, Farnborough and Harwell. The bombs destroyed forty-six training aircraft at Brize Norton, and the radar station at Ventnor on the Isle of Wight was attacked once more.

There had been many deeds of heroism that morning, but the whole world would soon know about one in particular. Shortly before noon, Flight Lieutenant James Nicolson of No. 249 Squadron was patrolling near Southampton when his Hurricane was attacked by a Messerschmitt 110. Cannon shells wounded Nicolson in the leg and eye and set his aircraft on fire, yet he remained in the blazing cockpit and managed to shoot down his attacker before baling out, severely burned. His exploit would later be recognised by the award of the Victoria Cross.

In the afternoon the *Luftwaffe* had sent out a force of bombers to attack the fighter airfields north of the Thames – Debden, Duxford, North Weald and Hornchurch – but the raid had been frustrated by bad weather and the raiders had returned to their bases with their bombs still on board, unable to find their targets through a thick blanket of cloud. Above the clouds, however, the weather was fine, and there were many combats across southern England as the German bombers roved across the country in search of their objectives. Forty-five German aircraft failed to return from operations on this day, a day that also cost the RAF twenty-one Spitfires and Hurricanes.

Now, as afternoon turned to evening, Armstrong had a strange feeling that the *Luftwaffe* would be active during the night, most likely sending over single raiders to attack any targets of opportunity their crews might be able to spot through breaks in the cloud layer. It was an ideal time, with no moon to silhouette the raiders against the carpet of cloud below them. He had voiced his opinion several times during the day to the senior air staff officer at HQ No. 12 Group, under whose control the Intruder Squadron had been placed while it was at Bircham Newton, and had sought approval to mount offensive operations over Holland, from whose bases he was sure the raiders would come. The approval had not been forthcoming; the Intruder Squadron was to be held in reserve.

In reserve for what? Armstrong had wondered, staring at the telephone at the end of his last call to Watnall, the location of No. 12 Group's HQ near Nottingham. Why couldn't his Blenheims at least be released to carry out night patrols? These were the responsibility of 12 Group's two Blenheim night-fighter squadrons, No. 23 at Collyweston near Stamford and No. 29 at Digby, with perhaps twenty aircraft between them; another six would make a substantial contribution to the Group's night defence effort. He resolved to try again later on.

His thoughts were still on the matter when a call came over the tannoy, instructing his squadron to come to readiness. He made a quick call to the dispersal, where Kalinski had remained on duty, and asked what was going on. The Pole confessed that he had no idea; all he knew was that someone was flying over from Watnall to deliver a briefing.

Mystified, Armstrong and Baird hurried down to their dispersal. In due course a de Havilland Dragon Rapide liaison aircraft arrived, and Armstrong went down to the watch office to greet its passenger, a wing commander. His name was Dickson, and he carried a bulky folder which, Armstrong discovered, contained maps of Holland and north-west Germany. He took Dickson to the dispersal hut and they closeted themselves away in Armstrong's office, together with Baird and Kalinski.

'I expect you're wondering what this is all about,' Dickson said. He was a small, quietly-spoken man with a deep scar curving down the right side of his face. It drew the corner of his mouth up in a perpetual half smile. 'I know you've been kept in the dark, and I'm sorry about that. It's just that we had to make certain that the weather was going to be favourable tonight. You see, the bomber boys are laying on their biggest effort so far. One hundred and fifty Blenheims, Hampdens, Whitleys and Wellingtons are setting out to attack the Ruhr, Frankfurt and even more distant targets such as Augsburg, as well as airfields in Holland. You'll understand now why we couldn't give a hint of anything over the 'phone, not even the secure line.

'The plan is to tickle up the Huns good and proper,' Dickson continued, 'and show them that they don't have things all their own way. Now, I can hear you asking, where do you come in?'

He spread out a map on Armstrong's desk top. 'The thing is, during the past couple of weeks bomber crews have been reporting interceptions by enemy night-fighters, which is something new. They haven't paid much attention to night defence so far. But just recently, there have been attacks in the areas I've circled, here, and if you look closely you'll see that each area has an airfield in it – a fighter airfield, moreover. There's Gutersloh, here, which seems to be the main base, but most of the attacks seem to have occurred over Holland, near Gilze-Rijen and Deelen, up here in the North.'

Dickson paused, lit a cigarette, blew out a stream of smoke and looked at Armstrong apologetically. 'Sorry, old boy, should have asked if you minded. It's your office, after all.' Armstrong grinned, shook his head and fished out his pipe, which he proceeded to fill while Dickson went on talking.

'What the Huns appear to be doing,' the wing commander said, 'is trying to catch the bombers en route to Germany. They are staying clear of the Ruhr itself, and

I don't think it's merely a matter of avoiding their own flak. I think it's something to do with what Goering reportedly said. Have you heard his famous boast?'

Armstrong and the others shook their heads. 'Well, just before the outbreak of war he apparently told his chums, in public, that no enemy bomber would ever fly over the territory of the Reich. In fact, he said that if one ever did, people could call him 'Meyer'. You know what's significant about that, of course.'

Their blank looks told him that they did not. 'Meyer,' Dickson explained, 'is a Jewish name.' He had no reason to elaborate further. They had all heard stories of what the Nazis were doing to the Jews.

'So,' Dickson went on, 'fatty Goering seems to have egg on his face, because our bomber boys have been flying over his Reich since day one. It looks as though he has given orders for increased night-fighter activity, which could cause a problem or two. The trouble is, we don't yet know anything about his night-fighter strength, or even what type of aircraft the Huns are using. The bomber crews that have reported interceptions up to now didn't even see what it was that attacked them. Which is why we, er, we'd like you chaps to nip across and find out.'

Armstrong and his fellow officers looked at one another and said nothing. Dickson looked slightly uncomfortable. After a moment or two of silence, he said, 'What I mean is, we – that is to say, Bomber Command – have asked us if we will send you over ahead of the bombers to patrol the Hun night-fighter bases in Holland and tempt their fighters up. We need to know if they are using some form of warning and control system similar to our own radar, so if they are already up and waiting for you it probably means that they are. You are free to work out your own tactical procedures, of course,' he added hastily. 'It's not as if we are asking you to stick your head into a noose.'

'Well, nobody lives for ever,' Kalinski remarked philosophically, 'and every noose has a particular hangman at the other end of the rope. Do we know who our hangman is?'

'If you mean do we know who is at the head of the German night-fighter force, Captain, all I can say is that our 'Y' Service people have picked up enemy radio signals that refer to a Colonel Kammhuber. He appears to be in overall command. We don't know who the operational commanders are, though.'

They are likely to be very good, Armstrong thought as he saw Dickson back to his aircraft a few minutes later, whoever they are.

As Dickson's pilot started the Rapide's engines, the wing commander paused before getting in and shook Armstrong's hand. 'Good luck tonight,' he said. 'I'm sorry to drop this one on you, but it really is important. If the Jerries are building up a strong night-fighter force, and they get on top of the bombers, then we won't be able to strike back at them without taking unacceptable losses, and they'll have won. It's as simple as that. We need to know.'

Armstrong watched the biplane fly away, then went back to the dispersal hut to work out the details of the operation with his two flight commanders before briefing the other crews. He had already decided not to tell them that they would be setting out on what might well prove to be a suicide mission.

The sun had already been set for an hour and a half when Armstrong led his six Blenheims away from Bircham Newton at 23.00, although the almost unbroken cloud cover gave a false illusion of darkness. Armstrong climbed steadily through the grey layer, his instruments giving off a faint and ghostly light; a brighter glare came from the Blenheim's engine exhaust stubs, and he resolved to have a word with Bircham Newton's engineer officer about that. Perhaps baffles of some sort could be fitted.

At 8,000 feet the Blenheim broke through the cloud layer into clear sky. The night was luminous, the August stars almost close enough to touch. A triad of planets lay from south to east across the heavens; brilliant Jupiter in the south-east, then red Mars, almost as brilliant but lower down, and finally Saturn, the least brilliant of the three. Armstrong pointed the Blenheim's nose at the latter, a beacon that guided him steadily along his easterly track, and climbed gently to 15,000 feet. The object of the exercise, he told himself, although it went entirely against his natural instinct, was to let the enemy know he was there.

'Everything okay, Kersh?' he queried. 'Dutch coast coming up.'

'Okay, skipper. We seem to be on our own so far.'

The cloud layer was beginning to break up below them, and Armstrong saw the starlight glinting on an expanse of water, broken by a long island with a hook-like tip at its western end. He identified it at once as Overflakkee and flew along its length, realising that if he held this course he would arrive directly over Gilze-Rijen, which lay between Breda and Tilburg. There had been no flak so far, and that fact alone made him feel uneasy. He weaved the Blenheim from side to side as he flew on, so that Kershaw could see into the blind spot below the tail. The other Blenheims would also be approaching their respective patrol stations by now, he thought. They ought to be stirring up some sort of reaction. The continued absence of flak and searchlights was an anxiety that continued to grow, fuelling the tension he was feeling.

Sixty miles north-west of Armstrong's aircraft, near Den Helder, a young *Luftwaffe* technical officer spoke quietly into a microphone, his face glowing an unearthly green in the light of the cathode ray tube in front of him. The information it displayed came to him via a Freya radar scanner, its tall, square-cut latticework of aerials pointed towards the English coast. The Freya could tell him the direction and range of the incoming aircraft, but not its altitude; the fighter pilot he was in contact with would need to work that out for himself, and the calculation would require a good deal of pure luck.

But if anyone was to succeed, that man would be

*Hauptmann* Heinrich Wolff, the commanding officer of the night-fighter *Gruppe* based at Gilze-Rijen. He had taken off half an hour earlier, acting purely on a hunch that the Tommies would be coming tonight, and now the Freya had confirmed it. Another hunch told him that the Tommy the radar had picked up would be flying at between 4,000 and 6,000 metres, so he levelled his Messerschmitt 110 at 5,000 and headed towards the spot in the sky where his agile brain calculated that the enemy aircraft would be in three minutes' time, if it held its course, and told his wireless operator/gunner, Buchholz, to keep his eyes open.

Fortune was definitely on Wolff's side that night. As he cruised over Dordrecht, peering into the night, he spotted twin pinpricks of light, slightly off to the left and some distance above. Alerting Buchholz, he increased speed and crept closer; the pinpricks of light were the glowing exhausts of a twin-engined aircraft.

Careful now, Wolff told himself. There must be no repetition of what had happened a couple of weeks earlier, when one of his pilots had returned to base jubilantly claiming to have shot down a Whitley bomber. But the Whitley was another Me 110; the twin fins, common to both aircraft, had confused him and led to tragedy. Neither of the 110's crew had escaped, and the pilot responsible, mortified and distraught, had shot himself.

As he drew closer, a horrible doubt assailed Wolff's mind. He could see the dark silhouette of the other aircraft, and it looked very much like that of a Junkers 88. He had to make absolutely certain.

Pushing open the throttles, he drew off to one side and overhauled the dark shadow until he was stationed off its right wingtip. He looked at it, straining his eyes for some clue as to its identity. A sudden glint of light showed on its upper fuselage and he realised with a sudden shock that he was looking at a gun turret, and that it was turning so that its guns pointed towards him.

Junkers 88s did not have an upper gun turret. The other aircraft was a Blenheim.

He turned away, standing the Messerschmitt on its wingtip and pulling the aircraft round hard through 360 degrees. The Blenheim was still there, but it was now diving towards the clouds. Red tracer lanced at him, passing just above the cockpit, and he dived at full throttle, dropping below the British aircraft until he was practically under the tail. He, like all other *Luftwaffe* fighter pilots, knew all about the Blenheim's vulnerable blind spot.

The Blenheim suddenly pulled out of its dive and began weaving, the manoeuvre taking Wolff by surprise, so that he almost overshot. Throttling back to match the Blenheim's speed and turning with it, he centred the dark shape in his gunsight and let fly with his full armament of two 20-mm cannon and four 7.9-mm machine guns.

The effect was almost instantaneous, and dramatic. A great sheet of blinding white flame poured back from the Blenheim's port wing and the aircraft turned over on its back, spinning down towards the broken cloud layer. A few moments later the whole wing broke away and dropped into the cloud, trailing burning fuel, followed by the rest of the aircraft. Wolff did not see any parachutes.

In England, a section of the RAF's 'Y' radio listening service, charged with the task of monitoring enemy fighter transmissions but also, on this night, instructed to listen to the Intruder Squadron's radio frequency, picked up a brief, despairing cry: 'We are under attack. We are being attacked by a Messerschmitt one-one-oh. I repeat, an Me one-one-oh. We are —' The transmission was abruptly cut off.

Wolff watched the glow in the clouds fade away and suddenly realised that he had forgotten, in his excitement, to call base with news of his victory. He did so now, and was informed by the controller that another contact had been picked up south of his present position. Wolff at once turned in that direction, clenching his eyes tightly shut for a moment; the glare of the burning Blenheim had temporarily ruined his night vision.

Fifteen miles away, still on patrol in the vicinity of Gilze-Rijen, Armstrong and Kershaw had witnessed the burst of fire in the sky and had watched what was clearly a blazing aircraft, falling towards the clouds with what seemed incredible slowness and breaking into fragments as it fell. With a leaden feeling in his stomach, Armstrong knew instinctively that it was one of his own. A savage desire for revenge almost overcame his sense of reason;

then it passed just as swiftly, and a cool sense of purpose infused him. He turned his Blenheim towards the spot where the burning aircraft had been extinguished in the clouds.

Just then, Kershaw's voice sounded over the intercom. 'Skipper, something's happening in our five o'clock. There's a light shining in the clouds. Could be a searchlight. Doesn't seem to be moving, though.'

Armstrong was already starting to turn the Blenheim back on to its original heading before the gunner had finished speaking. As the nose came round, he saw a pool of diffused white light over in the direction of Gilze, and immediately realised what it signified.

'Somebody's lost,' he said. 'They're using a searchlight as a homing beacon, shining it on the cloud base. I'm going to take a look. Going down now.'

He descended into the cloud, feeling his way cautiously, glad that there were at least no hills to worry about. Although it was several miles away the powerful searchlight beam illuminated the vapour ahead, turning it into pearly tendrils. Small, dancing rainbows came to life briefly, refracted from the water droplets that formed the cloud, then vanished as the Blenheim overtook them. In the searchlight's odd effect, rainbows also surrounded the arc of the Blenheim's propellers, lending an eerie, surreal air to the scene.

Suddenly, the Blenheim popped out of the cloud base, revealing a landscape bathed in light. Ahead, and to the left, the searchlight speared up like a brilliant blue-white finger, spreading out into a softer pool where the clouds blocked it. At its base, Armstrong knew, was Gilze-Rijen. He narrowed his eyes against the brilliance, looking for the aerodrome's flare path, but could not see it.

'Aircraft two o'clock, high!'

Kershaw's urgent call caused Armstrong to jerk his head round to the right. He looked up and saw it at once: the cruciform shape of an aircraft, dropping down from the clouds a few hundred feet higher up, silhouetted darkly against the glow. It was a Messerschmitt 109.

'That's their customer,' he said, watching as the other aircraft descended towards Gilze. 'Let's go and get him!'

Opening both throttles wide, he began to shadow the Me 109, following its every move as it continued its descent. It was flying very slowly, with undercarriage and flaps lowered. It turned a few degrees left and Armstrong realised that the pilot's intention was to circle the searchlight beam to get his bearings before setting himself up for a landing. The slight left turn brought the 109 even closer to the Blenheim, which was now coming within range. The enemy pilot was clearly unaware of the British aircraft's presence, as he made no attempt to take evasive action.

The distance closed steadily until only 250 yards separated the two aircraft. Lit up by the unmoving searchlight, the 109 looked like a moth, heading for a gigantic candle flame.

At 200 yards, from dead astern, Armstrong opened fire with a long burst, seeing his tracers converge on the Messerschmitt's fuselage in the area of the cockpit. The searchlight went out, plunging the world into darkness, but it no longer mattered. A great balloon of flame burst from the Messerschmitt, engulfing it almost completely, and one of its wheels broke away, hurtling back in the slipstream and narrowly missing the Blenheim's nose. Then the German fighter went down vertically, exploding with a vivid flash as it hit the ground. Showers of sparks that were fragments of burning wreckage scattered in all directions, glowing dully as they burnt themselves out. The usual acrid stink of gunsmoke drifted through the Blenheim.

'Break LEFT, Skipper!'

Kershaw's Vickers gun chattered even as his urgent cry sounded in Armstrong's headphones and the pilot turned the spectacle grip of the control column in the direction indicated, standing the Blenheim on its port wingtip and then pulling back on the control column so that the aircraft entered a steep, violent turn. What sounded like a massive barrage of hailstones caused the aircraft to shake violently and for a moment he thought that he might lose control, then he relaxed his grip on the stick and the vibration ceased.

A black shadow hurtled past, terrifyingly close, chasing the stream of fire that poured from its nose. Armstrong caught a glimpse of twin engines and twin fins, and knew what his attacker was even before a breathless Kershaw identified it as an Me 110. He continued his turn and then, levelling out, climbed hard for the shelter of the clouds.

Wolff was certain that he had hit his target. Intent on finishing it off, he too climbed into the clouds, flying a series of courses that took him towards the coast, searching the valleys and troughs between the cloud banks. He found nothing, even though his search took him halfway over the North Sea. Disappointed, he flew back to Gilze-Rijen. He would have to be content with his one victory. He hoped that the other night-fighters airborne that night had enjoyed some luck, too.

# Chapter Ten

Light stabbed at Armstrong's eyes. He opened them a fraction, moaned in pain, closed them quickly, and turned over in bed, facing away from the source of his discomfort.

'It's six o'clock,' a female voice informed him. 'You'd lie in bed 'til the sun burns your eyes out, you would.'

Armstrong rolled over again, groaning. The owner of the voice was standing by the window, adjusting the curtains she had just opened. She turned to face the bed, whose occupant made a half-hearted attempt to sit up, and failed.

'Oh, God,' Armstrong mumbled. 'Who'd have a bedroom that faces east?' He swallowed hard, wondering where the sawdust came from that seemed to be clogging his throat and finding it hard to talk past the swollen, foreign object that blocked his mouth. Reason told him that it must be his tongue. 'What happened? Oh, no, Phyllis, don't tell me. I don't think I want to know.'

'I'll tell you anyway,' Phyllis said. 'You got beastly, stinking drunk, that's what. Goodness only knows how much beer you had, and then whisky on top of that. You were sick on the landing, and then you tried to have a pee in my wardrobe. Fortunately, you couldn't manage it, although you obviously thought you had, because you were pulling at a coat hanger, wondering why it wouldn't flush. I managed to get you to the WC and left you there. The last I saw of you, you were curled around the pedestal, fast asleep. You must have come to bed in the early hours.'

'Oh, Lord,' Armstrong moaned, 'I'm sorry, Phyllis. I really am. Did I . . . I mean, did we —'

Phyllis laughed. 'Don't be ridiculous! You weren't capable of raising a smile. There was me, looking forward to your visit ever since you phoned, and all you did was get yourself blotto. Your chum wasn't far behind you, either. I ought to throw the pair of you out. Bad for my reputation, you are.'

Armstrong knew that the threat was an idle one. He had been seeing Phyllis, who was landlady of the Blue Bells Inn on the southern outskirts of Cambridge, on and off since the month war broke out – he had been attached to a Bomber Command station, nearby RAF Fordingham, at the time – and they had developed a deep affection for one another. Neither was under any illusion; Phyllis knew that Armstrong would never take her anywhere near an

Officers' Mess, and Armstrong knew that Phyllis wouldn't mope for long if he kissed her goodbye and never saw her again. She was a few years older, perhaps in her middle thirties, with a figure that made his senses reel. She also had the bluest eyes he had ever seen, crowned by sleek blonde hair. He had often wondered why she had never been snapped up, but he had never asked, and she had never volunteered any information about her past life, except that she had inherited the pub from her father.

Armstrong managed to sit upright in bed, his mouth making strange noises over which he seemed to have little control.

'What happened to Dickie last night?' he queried. Phyllis came and sat on the edge of the bed, pulling her dressing gown around her.

'He went off to see Doris,' she told him. 'I don't suppose we'll see *him* today.'

'Doris? Oh, yes, I remember.' Baird had formed an attachment with a young widow whose husband, also in the Fleet Air Arm, had been lost when the carrier HMS *Glorious* had been sunk by the battlecruisers *Scharnhorst* and *Gneisenau* off Norway the previous June. The attachment was, as yet, purely platonic – Doris's memories were still too fresh – but time was a great healer, and the intrepid Baird was doing his best.

Phyllis smiled suddenly, and leaned over to kiss his forehead. 'You're a real twerp, you are, but I can't help forgiving you. I'll go and make us some tea. I'm going to open that window wider, though; it smells like a brewery in here.'

Armstrong clasped his hands behind his throbbing head and lay back, closing his eyes and feeling the warmth of the early morning sun on his cheek. Notwithstanding the hangover, he felt as though he'd had a good night's sleep, untroubled by the dreams that had tormented him since that nightmare flight back from Holland a few nights before. The Me 110 had done more damage to his Blenheim than he had thought: the starboard engine had packed in halfway over the North Sea and metal had begun to peel away from the wing where the German bullets had punched holes. When he reached Bircham Newton and lowered the undercarriage, one leg had refused to come down and the other could not be retracted again, making a belly landing out of the question. He had been forced to touch down on one wheel, holding the damaged wing up as long as possible until the Blenheim had lost speed. The wing had settled to the ground, dragging its tip along the runway in a shower of sparks, and then the Blenheim had slewed on to the grass and collapsed on its belly as the good undercarriage leg folded under the strain. He and Kershaw had been lucky to get out in one piece.

It was not the strain of the flight back and the subsequent crash landing, however, that had brought the bad dreams. The recurring feature in them was Baird's face. The Scot had returned some minutes earlier; Armstrong had found him in the crew room with Copeland, his gunner, drinking tea laced with rum. Baird's face had been chalk white, except for the red ridge across his cheeks and nose caused by the tightness of his oxygen mask.

'They're all gone, Ken.' The words had been spoken very quietly, as though from a long way off. 'They are all gone. We are the only ones left.'

It was not quite true. Kalinski had got back, wounded in the shoulder and his gunner dead, putting his bullet-torn aircraft down in a field near the coast; but the others were gone. McIver and Smith, Winters and Redmond, both had fallen in flames over Holland, victims of the marauding night fighters; Van Berg had sent out a distress call, saying that he was having to ditch in the North Sea. Nothing further had been heard from him or his gunner, Jordison.

Four Whitleys, two Hampdens and a Wellington of the bomber force had also been lost that night; but Bomber Command had the information it wanted now, bought by the Intruder Squadron's sacrifice.

Group Captain Crosby, Bircham Newton's station commander, sensing the anger and despair of the survivors, had wisely taken it upon himself to pack them off on seventy-two hours' leave, promising to deal personally with any objections from Group or Fighter Command. And so, while Kershaw and Copeland had gone off to visit their respective families, Armstrong and Baird had decided that the best place to let off steam would be the Blue Bells, where the natives were exceedingly friendly.

Phyllis returned with two mugs of tea and a glass containing a liquid that fizzed. 'Here,' she said, thrusting it into Armstrong's hand, 'a glass of Eno's for you. It might just rescue what's left of your liver.'

Under Phyllis's watchful eye, Armstrong downed the salts in one go, then set the glass aside and gratefully sipped the scalding, sweet tea, feeling it gradually unclogging his mouth and throat. After the second mug, he was almost feeling like a human being again.

'I'll do some breakfast in a while,' Phyllis said, 'after I've bottled up. You can give me a hand, if you like. I expect you'll be wanting a bath to clear the cobwebs, so you can use the bathroom first, if you like.'

Armstrong shook his head. 'No, you have first go. I'll just brush my teeth, then I'm going for a run. That's the best way I know of getting rid of a hangover. Where's my bag, Phyl?'

'It's in the bottom of the wardrobe, and it's thanks to me that it's bone dry,' she said. Armstrong winced, then saw that she was grinning. All was well again.

The pilot enjoyed a morning run, whenever he had the chance; it was the one thing he had missed during his weeks in France. He always carried shorts, singlet and plimsolls in his kit. He eased his way out of bed, stretched a few times and put on his running gear quickly, picked up the spare key to the front door and went outside to face the morning, locking the door behind him.

During his visits to the Blue Bells he had discovered

several attractive paths, and he mentally selected the route he planned to take. He walked for a hundred yards to loosen his muscles and then set off at a steady jog, forcing himself over the first half-mile, which was sheer murder; then his natural bodily rhythm took over and before long he was running easily, his breathing regulated, feeling the first drops of sweat emerging from his pores.

He turned aside from the road onto a path that ran through some trees and then along the edge of a harvest field. Some men were already at work, and one or two who were regular customers of the Blue Bells waved at him as he passed.

'Feeling all right this morning, Ken?' one shouted.

'Don't know yet,' Armstrong replied. 'You can tell me what I got up to later on.'

The workmen laughed, and a few ribald comments drifted in his wake. He ran on, the sweat coursing down his face now, deliberately pushing himself hard so that his heart would pump blood faster round his body, cleansing it of the poisons he had inflicted on it the night before.

Armstrong ran for forty-five minutes, stopping a couple of times to do some stretch exercises, following a circular route that brought him back to the door of the inn. He unlocked it and went inside, hanging the spare key on a nail behind the bar, then went upstairs, feeling refreshed and fit. The bathroom door was ajar and he heard Phyllis humming to herself. He tapped lightly on the door and peeked inside to find the landlady towelling herself.

'Cheeky devil!' she exclaimed, looking round. 'Bursting in on a lady like that! Here, make yourself useful. Do my back.'

He did as he was told, taking the towel from her and rubbing lightly, moving down her spine and gently massaging her buttocks. Then he threw the towel onto the edge of the bath and turned her to face him, holding her and burying his face in her damp hair.

'Oh, you're all sweaty,' she murmured. She clasped her hands behind his back and pulled him tightly to her. Through his singlet, he could feel her nipples hardening. She had beautiful breasts, round and firm, with nipples, as he had once jokingly described them to her, like chapel hat-pegs. He slipped gently down on to one knee and, still holding her tightly, kissed them in turn, rolling his tongue around them. She dug her fingers deeply into his hair and made a soft little sighing noise.

He moved his face downwards, his tongue flickering briefly in her navel. She smelled of violets. He took a moment to glance up at her, mischievously; she was gazing down at him, her lips slightly open, and he knew that it was time. He rose swiftly, picked her up, kicked the bathroom door wide open and carried her through into the bedroom. She lay on the bed, watching him as he quickly stripped off.

They held each other for a while, indulging in long

kisses, and then she took him in her hand and drew him into her. Until that moment he had not fully realised the extent of his arousal and he came almost at once in a great surge that left him weak. She wrapped her legs around him and held him in her, moving under him, until she came too, and it was not long before she did. He took a strange comfort from the fact, for her urgency seemed to indicate that there had been no one other than himself in the time since he had last been with her. He had no reason to believe that there had been, but his nature was such that there was always a doubt, a tiny sore of what might just be jealousy, at the back of his mind.

Afterwards, they lay side by side for a few minutes, their fingers interlocked. It was Phyllis who broke the spell, pushing herself up on one elbow and smiling down at where he was beginning to stir again.

'You can put *that* away, my lad,' she said firmly. 'I've got work to do. Go on, off you go and have your bath – there won't be much hot water left, mind – while I do my hair and sort out some breakfast.' Her face was suddenly serious. 'You didn't use anything,' she said. 'You really should have, you know. Oh, well, I expect it'll be all right.' She leaned over and kissed him on the cheek. 'Anyway,' she added, 'I wouldn't care, if it was yours.'

He lay there for a while longer, smiling, realising that Phyllis had just paid him an amazing compliment, then went to have his bath. By the time he went down for his breakfast, he noticed that the sky had clouded over.

Opening the back door, he stood on the threshold and sniffed; he could smell rain in the air.

'Looks as though it's going to be set in for the day,' he said as they ate. 'Well, at least our chaps may get a bit of a rest.'

Had Armstrong but known it, some of the *Luftwaffe* formations engaged in the air attacks on England needed a rest, too. Two days before – Sunday, 18 August – the RAF had destroyed seventy-one German aircraft for the loss of twenty-seven of its own fighters. The RAF fighters had shot down eighteen Stukas that day, and sent as many more limping home damaged, a loss that caused the German High Command to withdraw the Junkers dive-bomber from the battle. The Me 110 squadrons had suffered almost as badly, losing fifteen aircraft; that brought the number of Me 110s shot down in a week of operations over England to seventy-nine. From now on, the orders specified, the Me 110s were to be used only on missions that were beyond the range of the single-engined Me 109 – or else they were themselves to be provided with a single-engined fighter escort. For the men who flew Messerschmitt's much-vaunted 'destroyer', it was the ultimate humiliation – and an act of tactical lunacy, for it meant that fewer fighters would from now on be available to escort the bomber formations.

But the week's air battles had seen Fighter Command hard hit, too, with one hundred and three Hurricanes and Spitfires lost in six days. No. 11 Group, in the front line, had suffered particularly badly, with forty-four pilots killed and twenty wounded in six squadrons – a casualty rate of 50 per cent. These battered squadrons were now withdrawn to rest and re-equip, and were replaced by others from airfields in the north.

But other squadrons were now being drawn into the battle. Sunday's air fighting had seen the first operations by No. 1 (Canadian) Squadron, and soon it would be the turn of the Poles of No. 302 Squadron at Leconfield, whose pilots were itching to get at the Germans. It was no longer Britain's battle alone, and to illustrate the point the battles of Sunday last had seen the death in action of a young pilot officer called Billy Fiske. More accurately, his name was William Meade Lindsley Fiske III, and he was an American, a wealthy stockbroker who had broken every kind of regulation to join the RAF on the outbreak of war. One of his fellow pilots said of him:

*Unquestionably Billy Fiske was the best pilot I've ever known . . . it was unbelievable how good he was. He picked it up so fast, it wasn't true. He had flown a bit before, but he was a natural as a fighter pilot. He was also terribly nice and extraordinarily modest. He fitted into the squadron (No. 601, Hurricanes) very well. The day Tangmere was bombed, Billy Fiske was airborne with the rest of us. We were up at twenty thousand feet and came down to chase the Ju eighty-sevens, which had dropped their bombs and were going out to sea. We went after them. When we'd exhausted our ammunition and were low on petrol, we returned to the aerodrome and landed. As I came down, I saw one of our aircraft on its belly, belching smoke. It must have got a bullet in its engine.*

*I taxied up to it and got out. There were two ambulancemen there. They had got Billy Fiske out of the cockpit. He was lying on the ground there. The ambulancemen didn't know how to take his parachute off, so I showed them. Billy was burned around the hands and ankles, so I told them to put on Tanafax, the stuff we were supposed to put on burns. I'm told now it's one of the worst things you could put on a burn. I told Billy, 'Don't worry, you'll be all right,' got back in my aeroplane and taxied back to the squadron. Our adjutant went to see him in hospital at Chichester that night. Billy was sitting up in bed, perky as hell. The next thing we heard, he was dead. Died of shock.*

Where Billy Fiske had led, others would follow: many of them, some arriving in the guise of Canadians.

Armstrong spent the morning helping Phyllis with her chores, feeding the chickens she kept on the small plot of land behind the inn and repairing some fencing. By noon it was drizzling heavily, and an hour after opening time there were next to no customers in the bar. Most of the regulars, Armstrong knew, were farmhands, and they would be working flat out to get the harvest in in case the weather turned really bad.

At two o'clock Phyllis locked the door, then she and Armstrong tidied the bar and went to bed, determined to make the most of the pilot's relatively short stay. At four o'clock their coitus was rudely interrupted by a loud

Armstrong stuck his head out of the window to see Baird standing on the step, soaking wet and looking utterly dejected. Armstrong pulled on his shorts and trousers and, leaving Phyllis to get dressed in her own good time, went downstairs to let the naval officer in.

A chill had set in, and while the kettle was boiling Armstrong lit the kitchen fire, which was already laid. He made some tea, taking a cup upstairs for Phyllis, then came and sat with Baird. The latter lit a cigarette and surveyed Armstrong through a cloud of smoke.

'You're a lucky beggar, you are,' he said. 'Phyllis is one in a million. Wish I had a Phyllis.'

Armstrong sighed. 'All right, then, let's have it. Things gone wrong between you and Doris?'

Baird flicked some ash into the fire. 'I don't know, that's the trouble. We were having a nice time; we went to the afternoon matinee and I asked her if I could go on seeing her, you know, if she'd be my regular girl, and she just burst into tears and ran off. Told me to leave her alone. I didn't know what to do, so I came back here. I really think a lot about her, you know. Can't help feeling pretty fed up.'

'Dickie, you really are a clot!'

Baird turned in his chair, blushing, not realising that his confession had been overheard by Phyllis, who had just entered the room.

'Yes, you are,' she said, forestalling any possible protest. 'For one thing, it's only a few weeks since the poor girl lost her husband, and here you are going at her like a bull at a gate. It's far too soon to ask her to make any regular commitment. Take her some flowers, say you're sorry for being such a pest, and stay friends. In a few weeks' time, well, who knows? She obviously likes you, or she wouldn't have agreed to go out with you. God, you men! I despair of you. And you can wipe that smirk off your face, after last night,' she added, throwing the words at Armstrong with a severity he knew she didn't mean.

'Might not be here in a few weeks,' Baird said miserably. Phyllis shook her head.

'You really have got it bad, haven't you? I think you need something to cheer you up.' She disappeared in the direction of the bar and came back with a large brandy, which she handed to Baird. He thanked her and took a sip. Armstrong looked from the glass to the landlady, and back again.

'Where's mine?' he asked.

'All you'll get is a clip round the ear, if you aren't careful. You can have a couple of beers after opening time, and then in moderation. I don't want any repetitions,' she warned.

The telephone rang. 'That'll be the brewery,' Phyllis said, and went off to answer it. But it wasn't the brewery, and a few moments later she returned to the kitchen, looking puzzled. 'It's for you,' she told Armstrong. 'Your adjutant, what's-his-name. Wouldn't say what he wanted.'

Armstrong went into the bar and picked up the phone.

'Is that you, sir?' a tinny voice asked at the other end. 'It's Briggs here. Splendid news, sir. It's Van Berg and Jordison. They've been picked up. They're dehydrated and a little weak, but all right otherwise. A minesweeper found them, apparently, drifting off the Dogger Bank. They're in hospital in Great Yarmouth. Hello, sir? Hello?'

It was some moments before Armstrong trusted himself to speak.

'Yes . . . yes, thank you, Briggsie. As you say, splendid news. Keep me informed. I'll be back the day after tomorrow.'

He returned to the kitchen and shared the news with Baird and Phyllis. The woman had no real idea of what the message meant, for Armstrong had told her nothing of the events of a couple of nights ago, but she recognised at once that it meant a lot to him.

'You'd better have that brandy after all,' she said.

It was still raining three hours later as they sat at the bar counter over a couple of pints and watched the first of the evening's customers appear. One of the men asked Phyllis if she would switch on the wireless; he had heard that the Prime Minister was due to make one of his speeches shortly. Armstrong and Baird, absorbed in quiet speculation about what the future might hold for them, took little notice as Winston Churchill's distinctive lisp sounded over the air; then they became conscious that a hush had descended on the room, and turned to face the radio set.

# THE INTRUDERS

*The gratitude of every home in our island, in our Empire, and indeed throughout the world, except in the abodes of the guilty, goes out to the British airmen who, undaunted by odds, unwearied in their constant challenge and mortal danger, are turning the tide of the world war by their prowess and their devotion. Never in the field of human conflict was so much owed by so many to so few.*

Armstrong glanced at Phyllis, who was furiously polishing a glass. She was trying very hard not to let him see that she was crying.

# Chapter Eleven

The two Hawker Hurricanes taxied carefully between newly-filled bomb craters on the much-battered surface of Manston aerodrome, following the directions of two airmen on motorcycles who led them to sandbagged revetments not far from where the Intruder Squadron's Blenheims had been parked on the eve of their first operation, an eternity ago. It was, in fact, a little over three weeks.

The ground crews who manhandled the Hurricanes into the dubious safety of the sandbagged enclosures stared curiously at them, for they were different from the Hurricanes that were still flying and fighting each day over southern England. For one thing, they were painted black overall; for another, they had a fuel tank under each wing. Finally, in place of the normal armament of eight machine guns, each aircraft was armed with two 20-mm Oerlikon cannon, their barrels extending menacingly from the leading edges of their wings.

Armstrong and Baird watched as ground crews draped camouflage nets over the two Hurricanes and then headed for a NAAFI van that had just drawn up. They obtained mugs of tea and some sandwiches, and waited for someone to come and collect them. Baird, Armstrong noted with relief, was restored to his former self, having received three or four long letters from Doris in the ten days since they had left the Blue Bells. Flowers, as Phyllis had suggested, had done the trick.

A lot had happened in those ten days. First of all, soon after his return to Bircham Newton, Armstrong had received a signal from Fighter Command HQ informing him that the Intruder Squadron would be re-equipped in a few weeks' time, although there was no hint of a definite date. Then his two reserve crews – who had never flown on intruder operations – had been transferred to the Coastal Command Blenheim squadron at Bircham Newton, while Kershaw and Baird's gunner, Copeland, had been ordered to report to RAF Middle Wallop, in Hampshire, for 'special training'.

Armstrong had been no less mystified when, on the following day – Friday, 23 August – he and Baird had received orders to report to the Aeroplane and Armament Experimental Establishment at Boscombe Down, near Amesbury in Wiltshire. An Avro Anson communications aircraft had come to pick them up and they had taken their full kit with them, for they had a feeling that they would not be returning to East Anglia.

Their perplexity was soon dispelled when they were shown a cannon-armed Hurricane that bore the serial number P2640, and a technical officer explained its background. It seemed that as long ago as 1938, the Air Ministry had decided to fit both Hurricanes and Spitfires with 20-mm cannon as soon as possible, and to this end four factories had been built to manufacture Hispano guns. Proposals to install four 20-mm cannon in the Hurricane had originated at Hawker Aircraft Ltd. in May 1939, and in the following month ground-firing tests had been carried out with two Oerlikon cannon fitted in the wings of a damaged Mk 1.

These were partially successful, and the wings were then fitted to a trials Hurricane Mk 1 – P2640, the aircraft shown to Armstrong and Baird – which flew on 7 June 1940. After air-firing trials at Boscombe Down, the aircraft had been allocated to No. 151 Squadron at North Weald early in August for operational evaluation, and on the 13th, a Flight Lieutenant Smith, flying it from Martlesham Heath, had destroyed a Dornier 17.

Apart from some problems with the guns jamming, there was no doubt that the cannon was a much more effective armament than the machine gun, and someone at Air Ministry had decided that Hurricanes converted in this way, and fitted with long-range fuel tanks, would be very useful as night intruders. Two more aircraft were being modified by Hawker Aircraft at Kingston, and would be ready for delivery by the end of August. The task of Armstrong and Baird was to pioneer their use on night operations over the continent.

The RAF's intruder and night-fighter activities were likely to become increasingly important during the coming weeks, for there were strong indications that the Germans were switching more and more to night operations. Despite the cloudy conditions, over 200 enemy bombers had attacked British targets on the night of 23/24 August, and over 100 on the following night.

On that night, something happened that was to change the face of the air war. A German bomber crew, briefed to attack the oil refinery at Thameshaven, mistakenly dropped their bombs on the city of London, a prohibited zone. The reaction of Hermann Goering was swift. Early the next morning, every unit that had taken part in the night's operations received a teleprinter signal from the *Reichsmarschall* himself:

*An immediate report is required identifying those crews who dropped bombs within the perimeter of London. Luftwaffe High Command will itself undertake the punishment of each aircraft captain involved. They will be posted to infantry regiments.*

Prime Minister Winston Churchill, seizing his opportunity to boost the morale of the British people, instructed RAF Bomber Command to attack Berlin by way of reprisal.

The attack was sanctioned by the War Cabinet, and on the night of 25 August a reluctant Bomber Command – who could see no strategic value in the operation – despatched 103 bombers on operations to Germany, half of them to Berlin. The crews found the German capital covered in thick cloud, which prevented accurate bombing. The only bombs that fell within the city limits of Berlin destroyed a wooden summer house in a garden in the suburb of Rosenthal, and two people were slightly injured. Many of the bombs fell into large farms in country areas south of the city. 'Now they're trying to starve us out,' the Berliners joked.

But for most Berliners, it was not a joke. Apart from one tiny pinprick of a raid carried out by a French bomber in June, this was the first time that bombs had ever fallen on Berlin. 'The Berliners are stunned,' American correspondent William L. Shirer noted in his journal on 26 August. 'They did not think it could ever happen. When this war began, Goering assured them it couldn't . . . They believed him. Their disillusionment today therefore is all the greater. You have to see their faces to measure it.'

When Air Vice-Marshal Keith Park summoned his station commanders, senior squadron commanders and controllers to a conference the following morning, they found the commander of No. 11 Group in an optimistic mood. 'Gentlemen,' he said, 'I don't know how much longer we can keep this up. But somebody has dropped bombs on Berlin.'

Only a few of those present guessed what Park meant. An attack on Berlin was almost certainly to be followed by *Luftwaffe* raids on London and other major cities – with a good chance that his vital fighter airfields might be left alone for a few precious days. Park's reasoning was correct. Adolf Hitler, stung into a response, thundered to an ecstatic female audience in the Berlin *Sportpalast*:

*Mr Churchill is demonstrating his new brainchild, the night air raid. Mr Churchill is carrying out these raids not because they promise to be highly effective, but because his air force cannot fly over German soil in daylight, whereas German planes are over English soil every day . . . Wherever the Englishman sees a light, he drops a bomb . . . on residential districts, farms and villages. For three months I did not answer because I believed that this madness would be stopped. Mr Churchill took this as a sign of weakness. We are now answering night for night. When the British air force drops three or four thousand kilograms of bombs, we will in one night drop two hundred, three hundred or four hundred thousand kilograms. When they declare they will increase their attacks on our cities, then we will raze their cities to the ground. We will stop the handiwork of these night pirates, so help us God . . . The hour will come when one of us will break, and it will not be National Socialist Germany!*

*In England they are filled with curiosity and keep asking, 'Why doesn't he come?' Be calm. Be calm. He's coming! He's coming!*

The ordeal of the cities was about to begin.

August had given way to September now, and as Armstrong and Baird sat beside their black-painted Hurricanes on the first evening of the new month and waited for darkness, they realised that it was Sunday evening. But across the country no church bells pealed, for the ringing of church bells was the signal that the invasion was on.

The previous two days had been hard ones for Fighter Command. On 30 August Biggin Hill had been completely wrecked, with sixty-five personnel killed and wounded; most of the damage had been done in a surprise low-level attack by eight Dorniers. The airfield was hit again the next day, again by Dorniers, while a second force of Dorniers swept over Hornchurch and released their bombs right on top of No. 54 Squadron's Spitfires, which were taxying out for take-off. The last flight, led by Squadron Leader Al Deere, was blown apart by a stick of bombs just as it was getting airborne. The three Spitfires were completely wrecked, but miraculously the pilots escaped with only minor injuries. The Biggin Hill squadrons, Nos. 72 and 79, were luckier: they were already airborne, and patrolling well to the south, when the bombers hit their airfield.

The position was beginning to look black for the RAF. There were no longer enough replacement pilots to fill the gaps, and to make matters worse the Germans were tightening up their fighter escort procedure. When eighteen

Heinkels of KG 1 attacked the docks at Tilbury on 1 September, they were escorted by three *Jagdgeschwader* – roughly four fighters to every bomber. The German aircraft returned to base without loss, having been virtually unmolested by the RAF.

The nights were beginning to lengthen now, Armstrong thought, as he smoked a last pipe and watched the afterglow of the sunset. It was seven o'clock. In an hour and a half, or thereabouts, the moon would be rising. It was waning towards its last quarter, and there would be plenty of light. The sky was clear, apart from some misty tendrils of cloud high up.

Out of the rising moon the bombers would come, heading for their targets in the South-West, Merseyside and the Midlands. The RAF's listening 'Y' Service had picked up indications that tonight's main thrust would come across the broad stretch of the Channel, from the direction of Cherbourg, and it was there, off the French coast, that the two Hurricanes would mount their patrol. As yet, because of their new armament, they were not cleared for operations over the continent itself.

Armstrong knew that Blenheims would be out tonight, attacking airfields in Holland, and after his own experience he did not envy them. But a diversion was necessary, because Bomber Command was mounting a maximum-effort operation again, with over 130 aircraft attacking targets in Germany and, once again, in Italy.

Armstrong looked at his watch and then at the dark

figures of the ground crew, who had been standing by for some time with their trolley-accs, ready to start the Hurricanes' Merlin engines. He tapped out his pipe, carefully ground out a few sparks of glowing tobacco underfoot, and put it in his tunic pocket. Underneath their tunics, he and Baird were wearing silk and wool aircrew vests and rollneck pullovers, with fleece-lined flying jackets as an outer covering; two thick pairs of thick woollen socks made their flying boots a tight fit, but it was a discomfort that had to be tolerated, for despite the warmth generated in the cockpit by the engine it would be bitterly cold at altitude over the sea.

'Come on, Dickie. Time to go.'

The *Luftwaffe* had left Manston alone for a week, since the attacks of 24 August, when it had been bombed five times; although the buildings were wrecked the airfield surface was once more serviceable, and although the fighters lurched uncomfortably over the ruts as they rolled across it, they became airborne without incident, climbing into a purple sky.

Armstrong revelled in the sheer pleasure of flying a single-seat, single-engined fighter again, even though the drag of the two fixed 44-gallon auxiliary fuel tanks made the Hurricane a little sluggish. He knew that Hawkers were experimenting with jettisonable tanks, but for the time being the fixed variety would make combat with enemy fighters a risky venture. They also reduced the Hurricane's top speed to about 300 m.p.h., which would make catching a fast German bomber like the Junkers 88 rather hard work.

The two Hurricanes, in loose formation, climbed steadily to 8,000 feet, the pilots keeping their navigation lights on as they flew south-westward across Kent. They switched the lights off as they crossed the Channel coast a little to the west of Beachy Head. A few moments later Baird drew alongside and waggled his wings, then peeled off on a new course that would take him to his own patrol area over the Bay of the Seine, between Cherbourg and Le Havre, sixty miles east of the point to which Armstrong was heading. The silhouette of his aircraft showed briefly against the eastern sky, which still retained a pastel shade of pale blue in the aftermath of the sunken sun, then vanished in the lengthening shadows.

Armstrong decided to stay at 8,000 feet; any higher, and – as trials had revealed – there was a risk of the cannon icing up. The Oerlikon cannon, which was drum-fed, used 20-mm ammunition made by the Kynock Armament Company and its cartridges were of softer brass than those made by Vickers. These expanded when the shell was fired, and were given an oily coating to aid extraction from the gun breech. Although icing was a problem, the Oerlikon gun – which was also used for anti-aircraft defence by the Royal Navy – was not prone to stoppages. The same could not be said of the other cannon under test by the RAF, the 20-mm Hispano. It had been fitted to the Spitfires of No. 19 Squadron at

Fowlmere for operational trials, and Armstrong had read the commanding officer's initial report while at Boscombe Down. It was not encouraging. Time and again, the Spitfire pilots had got within range of enemy aircraft, only to suffer the frustration of having their guns jam after only a few rounds had been fired. But once the snags had been ironed out, Armstrong was sure that the Hispano was the gun that would eventually be chosen for the fighters of the Royal Air Force; it had the advantage of being belt-fed. The Oerlikon's ammunition drums, which weighed sixty pounds when fully charged, carried fewer rounds.

Armstrong cruised on for half an hour until the tip of the Cherbourg peninsula appeared, ten miles off his port wing. A similar distance ahead, right in front of the nose, was the island of Alderney, which – like the rest of the Channel Islands – was now under the Nazi jackboot.

The light of the gibbous moon, with newly-risen Jupiter shining brilliantly close by, threw everything into stark relief. A shimmering path of moonlight across the water seemed to pursue Armstrong's aircraft as he started his patrol, following a fixed path that ran from north-east to south-west and back again. Overhead the summer stars blazed in all their glory, seen as earthbound beings can never see them, shrouded as they are by a canopy of haze and smoke. The constellations wheeled slowly across the sky each time Armstrong turned through 180 degrees at the end of each five-minute leg of his 'beat', the sprawled

'W' of Cassiopeia alternating with Libra's scales in front of the fighter's nose.

Armstrong scanned the eastern sky every few seconds, but there was no sign of the black dots of enemy bombers climbing out of Normandy, showing briefly like ink-spots against the faint ribbon of pale light in the east before reaching the sanctuary of the shadows. He glanced at his fuel gauges, assuring himself that there was still plenty left, and decided to extend his patrol line a little to a point beyond the Channel Islands.

Even that might not be far enough, he told himself. He had an odd hunch that the enemy bombers might be penetrating much further west tonight than they usually did, planning maybe to skirt the western fringe of Wales before turning in to attack Merseyside. If they made the Channel crossing from Brittany, rather than Normandy – say between Dinard and Brest – then a northerly heading would take them over the lightly-defended areas of the West Country and western Wales.

So Armstrong flew on towards the southwest, knowing that he was defying his own principles by not sticking to his plan. Brest was 140 miles from his designated patrol area; he could not break radio silence to tell anyone what he was doing, and if he came down in the sea no one would have the faintest idea where to look for him.

The thought struck him that at least some pilots, shot down over the Channel, must have drifted slowly out into the Atlantic, kept afloat by their lifejackets, despair replacing hope as the hours and even days went by, until they died miserably of hunger, thirst and exposure. He pushed the depressing picture from his mind and flew on, although he knew he was sticking his neck out, especially since he had no second engine to sustain him if the trusty Merlin ceased to function for any reason. He would impose a strict time limit, and at the end of it he would head for Cornwall, ninety miles to the north-west.

In one sense Armstrong's hunch was correct, although geographically he was a long way off target. Nearly two hours earlier, a large, four-engined aircraft had taken off from Bordeux-Merignac airfield, over 300 miles south of Armstrong's patrol area. It was followed by five more, at intervals of five minutes. The aircraft were Focke-Wulf FW 200s, military versions of the civil airliner that had plied the transatlantic routes in the years immediately before the War.

Dieter Wenninger was no stranger to the cockpit of the FW 200; he had flown the civil version on several occasions during his time with the German airline, Lufthansa. Someone at the German Air Ministry must have unearthed that fact, because at the beginning of August he had suddenly found himself transferred from the OKL Reconnaissance Group to an outfit called KG 40, which had just moved to France. KG 40 had already seen a lot of action against British shipping, and had also carried out experimental minelaying operations off British east coast ports, each aircraft carrying two unwieldy 1,000-kg devices.

Tonight's mission was different. Tonight, the Kondors – as the militarised FW 200s were known – were to pioneer long-range bombing operations against the British Isles. Their targets were Liverpool and Birkenhead, involving a round trip of around 1,100 miles and a flight time of some seven hours. The distance and airborne time presented no problem for the Kondor, which at economic cruising speed could stay aloft for fourteen hours. From time to time, Kondors took off from Bordeaux on weather reconnaissance missions that took them far out into the Atlantic, flying round the west coast of Ireland and northern Scotland to land at Stavanger, in Norway.

The Kondor's bomb load was not very big – four 250-kg bombs, carried under the wings – but that was no smaller than the load that could be lifted by the Dornier 17, and the Kondor's five-man crew could take heart from the fact that their aircraft carried a much better defensive armament than the Dornier: a 20-mm cannon in the nose and three MG 15 machine-guns to guard the tail.

Wenninger knew that the Kondor was a far from ideal solution to Germany's long-range bomber problems. For one thing, its structure was too weak, and the military version, which was heavier than its civil counterpart, had a tendency to break its back in a heavy landing. You had to be careful how you handled it, too: it was very easy to overstress the airframe in tight, evasive manoeuvres, with possible catastrophic consequences.

The leading Kondor crossed the French coast to the west of St Malo, flying at 10,000 feet, following a course that was almost due north. Wenninger was worried about the bright moonlight and absence of cloud cover, and ordered his gunners to keep a sharp lookout. It was nine-thirty, and there were still 300 miles to run before they reached the target area. The plan was to make landfall on the English coast near Weymouth, make a detour to skirt the defences of Bristol – which was scheduled to be under heavy attack by other *Luftwaffe* formations at about the same time – and approach the target over the full length of Wales.

Some distance to the west of the Channel Islands, Armstrong had decided to call it a night. He had exhausted his auxiliary tanks long ago, and his petrol gauge had started to fluctuate the moment he had changed to the main tank. It was probably nothing to worry about, but it was better to be safe than sorry. He turned north towards Lyme Bay. The English coast was seventy-five miles away, about twenty-five minutes' flying time at economical cruising speed. There were a number of airfields to the north of Lyme Bay where he could land and refuel.

A few minutes later, when he was within radio range, he contacted No. 10 Group Sector Control at Middle Wallop, identifying himself by means of a device called 'Pipsqueak', which transmitted a series of signals over his radio. The signals were picked up by direction-finding ground stations, which took cross-bearings to fix his position. There was a pause, and then the sector controller's urgent voice sounded in his headphones.

'Buckshot, turn right heading zero-four-five and climb to angels ten. We have possible trade for you, range one-five miles.'

Armstrong did as he was told, wondering for the umpteenth time who the hell thought up silly call signs, and hoping that whatever the controller wanted him to do, it wouldn't take long. Although the Merlin was still roaring healthily, the needle of the fuel gauge was still behaving oddly. There was silence for a while, then: 'Buckshot, make your heading zero-four-zero and go to angels twelve. We have definite trade.'

Armstrong climbed higher, looking around as he did so. Then he saw the other aircraft, etched briefly on a patch of pearly cloud above and to the left. He opened the throttle and went after it, knowing that every extra knot of speed was gobbling up his dwindling fuel supply.

He had no difficulty in keeping the aircraft in sight; the moonlight behind him saw to that. He was above it now, and its shape was clearly defined against the sea. As he crept closer, he saw that it had four engines, and a sudden doubt assailed him. He knew that Bomber Command had just taken delivery of a new four-engined bomber, the Short Stirling. He had studied aircraft recognition photographs and silhouettes of it. The Stirling had a single fin, too, like the aircraft in front of him.

And yet . . . the machine he was looking at seemed altogether less bulky than the British bomber. Its fuselage was too slender, its wings too long. He descended to the same altitude, still closing in, and saw that the strange aircraft had some sort of bulge under the fuselage, rather like the Heinkel 111's ventral gun position, but much longer. He was going to have to make up his mind quickly; the English coast was approaching fast, and in the distance he could already make out the long spit of land that was Portland Bill.

Suddenly, he knew the enemy for what it was. He shouted 'Tally ho!' over the radio and began his attack, dropping a little below the Kondor's tail and then pulling up the nose of the Hurricane, making fine adjustments until the German machine sat squarely in his gunsight. He stabbed his thumb down on the firing button, praying that the cannon would work. They did.

He had fired the cannon before, but during the daytime, and was prepared for the shuddering recoil. What took him by surprise were the vivid flashes of orange light that speared from the gun muzzles, temporarily blinding him. He squeezed his eyes shut, then opened them again. The Kondor was flying serenely on, with no visible sign of damage.

In the absence of tracer rounds, it was almost impossible to tell if he was hitting the target, which was now shooting back. Ignoring the red streaks that came at him from the gun positions above and below the fuselage, he dropped back a little, dived to gain speed, then pulled back the stick and climbed until his nose was pointing directly at the Kondor's underside. He fired again, ruddering so that the fighter's nose yawed from side to side, raking the aircraft from wingtip to wingtip. This time there was no mistake. Flashes of shell bursts erupted all over the German's dark silhouette, and a cloud of debris broke away from it. The ventral gunner abruptly ceased firing.

Armstrong dived away to get clear of the debris, and as he did so a bright glare lit up the interior of his cockpit. Climbing again, he turned and looked for his victim. A horrifying sight met his eyes.

A massive explosion had reduced the Kondor, laden as it was with fuel, to a cloud of debris. The wreckage spun wildly down towards the sea, and as it fell a stream of blazing fuel spewed out to form concentric circles around it, like a huge Catherine wheel. Armstrong watched for a few moments, then called up control. He suddenly felt desperately tired. Despite the cold, which was now bitter, he was covered in sweat.

'I got him. It was Focke-Wulf Kondor. There may be more. I'm just about out of fuel. Can you give me a course for the nearest airfield?'

'Good show, Buckshot. Steer zero-one-zero for Yeovilton. The Navy will be expecting you. And thanks.'

There was one survivor from the Kondor. Dieter Wenninger, knocked unconscious by the force of the explosion that destroyed his aircraft, had regained his senses to find himself falling through space, surrounded by burning debris. It took him long moments to realise what had happened, and that he was still alive. He scrabbled for the release ring of his parachute, tearing his fingernails bloody; then, to his horror, he remembered that he had not clipped the pack to his seat harness. There had been no time or opportunity.

It took an eternity to fall the last few thousand feet, but by the time he hit the water he felt nothing but a strange, fatalistic calm.

# Chapter Twelve

August had ended badly for the embattled squadrons of Fighter Command. The last day of the month had seen the destruction of thirty-nine RAF fighters – the biggest loss so far in a single day – against forty-one German aircraft shot down. The Luftwaffe continued to pound the fighter airfields. In an effort to protect them, the RAF sector controllers felt compelled to maintain standing patrols over the bases most likely to be hit, with the result that fewer fighters were available to engage the enemy off the coast. Committed piecemeal to the battle, the RAF suffered heavily. The second day of September was another black spot, with thirty-one Spitfires and Hurricanes lost and thirty-five German aircraft accounted for. On this day, for the first time since the battle began, a Messerschmitt 110 Geschwader – ZG 76 – was able to carry out an unopposed escort mission over southern

England. The crew, who were escorting the Heinkels of KG 53 in an attack on Eastchurch, reported that they had not seen a single RAF fighter in the air. The lack of opposition lent fresh courage to the Luftwaffe crews: at last it looked as though the final collapse of Fighter Command was imminent.

The optimism was short-lived, particularly where ZG 76 was concerned. On 4 September, a formation of its Messerschmitts, carrying bombs, was heading for an attack on the Hawker and Vickers Armstrong aircraft factories at Brooklands when the Hurricanes of No. 253 Squadron from Kenley fell upon them. The Squadron diary recorded the action:

*Nine Hurricanes took off from Kenley at 1305-1310 hours to patrol base and Croydon at 18,000 feet. They were flying squadron Vic formation when they sighted twenty Me 110s about to attack Brooklands aerodrome. Leader turned the formation ninety degrees to starboard and in shallow Vic dived to the attack out of the sun from about 12,000 feet. Flt Lt Cambridge, leading the forma-tion, attacked an enemy aircraft from the beam and above, expending all his ammunition in one long burst, and saw the target's port engine catch fire. Blue One followed it down and saw it crash in flames in a field.*

*Blue Two, Plt Off Samolinski, attacked another and observed a fire in the cockpit, after which the enemy aircraft turned and went into a dive. Green Two, Sgt Dredge, attacked a Me 110 from 30 degrees above and to the rear, giving a ten-second burst while closing from 300 down to 25 yards. Both engines caught fire and a red glow was observed in the cockpit, the enemy was seen to dive straight down and burst into flames (confirmed by Red One). Green Three, Plt Off Novak, after attacking an Me 110 observed smoke coming from the fuselage, after which the enemy dived and crashed.*

*Red One, Flt Lt Wedgewood, succeeded in getting on the tail of an Me 110 and fired a ten-second burst from 250 yards to point-blank range. The enemy caught fire, climbed steeply for a second, before falling to crash in a wood. Red Two, Plt Off Corkett, attacked an Me 110 which was flying on the starboard side of the enemy Vic; after two bursts the enemy broke formation, climbed 500 feet, turned over on its back and dived straight down and exploded in a field.*

*Red Three, Sgt Kee, delivered a head-on attack on an Me 110 from slightly below and from 250 yards closing to 50 yards, firing 1-2 second bursts. Small pieces ripped off the fuselage and tail. Blue Three, Sgt Innes, and Green One, Fg Off Watts, silenced the rear gunners of two Me 110s. Nine Hurricanes landed at Kenley 1355 hours. Our losses: nil. Enemy casualties: six Me 110s destroyed, one damaged.*

The Germans lost twenty-five aircraft in the day's fighting, and fifteen of them were Me 110s. But Fighter Command had also lost seventeen aircraft, and on the previous day the scores had been even, with both sides losing sixteen. It was the first time that losses and victories had matched one another. And despite the martyrdom of the Me 110s, some had got through to bomb the Vickers factory, where most of Bomber Command's Wellington bombers were being built. Only six bombs hit the factory, but they killed eighty-eight people and injured six hundred.

The situation was about to change. On 3 September, Hermann Goering visited The Hague for a conference with his two *Luftflotten* chiefs, Kesselring and Sperrle. There he told them that Hitler was pressing him to switch the main attacks onto London itself, as a reprisal for RAF attacks on Berlin. Damage had been negligible, but Hitler had vowed reprisals.

The plan was bitterly opposed by Sperrle, who rightly believed that it would be madness to switch the attacks away from the RAF's fighter airfields at this crucial stage of the battle. Kesselring, on the other hand, believed that the RAF was on the point of evacuating the hard-hit forward airfields and withdrawing to bases north and west of London, beyond the range of single-engined fighter escorts. In this case, Kesselring argued, the only sure way of destroying RAF Fighter Command was to overwhelm it in air combat. If the *Luftwaffe* mounted a large-scale assault on London, the RAF would be forced to throw its last reserves into the defence of the capital. This was the firm belief of 'Smiling Albert' Kesselring, the 55-year-old former army officer who had no first-hand experience of tactical air operations and who had only reluctantly accepted a transfer to the Air Force seven years earlier – and it was his argument that carried the day.

On the night of 5 September, seventy German bombers unloaded sixty tons of bombs onto the London docks. The die was cast, and London's agony was about to begin.

Meanwhile, there were ominous signs. For days now, barges, steamers, tugs, trawlers and motor boats – all the craft which the Germans had requisitioned over the preceding weeks – had been moving in a steady stream along the coast and inland waterways to their assembly areas in the occupied French Channel ports. RAF photo-reconnaissance aircraft, keeping a watch on the ports, reported that 115 barges were concentrated in Ostend harbour on 5 September; a week earlier there had been none. The *Luftwaffe's* bomber fleet was also being heavily reinforced.

A signal went out to all RAF units, placing them under Alert No. 2: it meant that an invasion was expected within the next three days. That night, aircraft of Bomber Command, Coastal Command and the Fleet Air Arm began a major offensive against the invasion ports, while at certain key points on England's south coast specialist troops waited to set the sea alight – perforated fuel pipes had been laid offshore, to confront the invaders with a wall of fire as they approached the beaches. And just in case the electronic ignition equipment failed, two Tiger Moth biplanes stood by at Manston, their pilots armed with nothing more than flare pistols, which they were to discharge from low level into the fuel-soaked sea . . .

Elsewhere, Blenheim bombers, singly or in pairs,

suddenly turned up at forward airfields along the coast and made rendezvous with sinister-looking vehicles that looked like fuel tankers, but were not. Protruding from the Blenheims' bomb bays were pipes that looked like the ends of garden hoses, but the spray they would discharge onto the heads of the invaders would be mustard gas, not water, and there were rumours of other more hideous agents, such as anthrax spores.

Britain would not go down without a fight; and those responsible for planning her last-ditch defence would use everything at their disposal to thwart the attackers.

The Germans were confident. During the first two days of September, the 'Invasion of England' was filmed for their newsreels in the harbour of Antwerp, with the holiday beach of St Anne representing a stretch of Britain's shoreline. Here, for two days, invasion barges drew in to the shore and troops leapt into the water as light tanks rolled off the craft into the shallows and ploughed their way towards the beach, firing as they went. The invasion, when it came, would be at night, or very early in the morning, and there would not be enough light to film the actual event. Most of the German public would be no wiser; it was action they needed. And it was for that reason that cameramen were assigned to the Air Fleets, to film the destruction of London that was to precede the invasion.

\*

# THE INTRUDERS

*Saturday, 7 September 1940: 15.30 Hours*

There was quite a champagne party in progress on the edge of the cliffs at Cap Gris Nez. The central figures were Hermann Goering and his two Marshals, Sperrle and Kesselring, surrounded by an entourage of staff officers, the whole under the watchful eye of heavily-armed field security police, there to make certain that no Frenchman with suicidal intent tried to bump off the *Luftwaffe's* top brass.

Goering, resplendent in pale blue and gold uniform, was in a jovial mood. Earlier in the day he had made a tour of some of his front-line fighter units, joking with 'the boys', telling them how easy a time they had of it in their speedy Me 109s, compared with the stick-and-wire biplanes he had flown in the previous war. They had laughed uproariously when he had tried to squeeze his bulk into the narrow confines of a 109's cockpit, and predictably failed. He liked to think that he was one of them, liked to think they were proud of having a C-in-C who had once commanded the élite Richthofen fighter wing, and who had twenty-two victories to his credit.

The clifftop picnic had been a huge success. Now all eyes were on the sky, where the first wave of 347 bombers was heading out over the Channel in a deafening thunder of engines. Above them their guardian Messerschmitts wheeled, glittering diamonds in the afternoon sun – over 600 of them, forming part of the greatest aerial armada the world had ever seen.

In the cockpit of one of the leading Heinkels, Cameraman (First Class) Jürgen Held of the *Luftwaffe* Film Unit was almost beside himself with excitement. He had flown before, but never on such an assignment as this. It was hot and uncomfortable in the bomber's glasshouse cockpit, but the mild discomfort didn't trouble Held; he was much too excited, and in any case he had work to do, filming the great formations of bombers that rose and fell slowly on the currents of warm air all around him.

He turned his head and looked at the navigator, who glanced up briefly from his chart and winked reassuringly, even though Held didn't feel at all jittery. The radio operator had closed down his station and was manning one of the bomber's defensive guns, the one firing forwards from the pannier below the fuselage. There were two more gunners, one operating the gun that fired rearwards from the pannier, guarding the spot under the tail, and another crouched under a cupola on top of the fuselage.

Over the pilot's shoulder, Held filmed the Thames estuary, its waters glistening in the sun 12,000 feet below. He could not resist looking round again, craning his neck for another view of the stepped-up echelons of Heinkels and Dorniers, strung out across the sky like dark birds of prey, with speedy Messerschmitts flashing over the serried ranks.

Held wore a flying helmet fitted with a long lead that was plugged into a spare socket, enabling him to move freely around the cockpit, although he was careful to avoid getting in anyone's way. Over the intercom, he heard the pilot warning the crew that the target would be coming up in ten minutes. The target was the London docks, situated in the great U-bend of the Thames in London's East End. The navigator, who was also the bomb aimer, crawled forward into the nose and began making adjustments to the bomb sight.

The bombers were crawling over a layer of broken cumulus cloud, through which landmarks showed up clearly. Looking down through one gap, Held picked out a large town; that must be Canterbury, he told himself, and looked for the cathedral, but could not see it. Feeling a little disappointed, he peered up through the cockpit roof, scanning the sky above and behind. So far, there was no sign of any British fighters. It was as though the whole of southern England was asleep. Well, Held thought gleefully, 300 loads of bombs would soon wake it up.

But the English were already awake, as he discovered a moment later when a shout from one of the tail gunners brought his heart leaping into his mouth.

'*Achtung*! Enemy fighters on the starboard beam, closing!'

Held stared wildly out of the cockpit, and saw nothing, just a line of black dots, sweeping across the sky above the white banks of cloud. Then he realised that the dots were the British fighters, whether Spitfires or Hurricanes he could not tell. Doing his best to steel his nerves, he gripped his cine-camera tightly and pointed it at the oncoming aircraft.

They were Spitfires, two squadrons of them, and they hurled themselves beam-on at the German bombers. A Spitfire whistled through the German formation, its sleek lines elongated by the speed, flashes twinkling along the leading edges of its wings. It was followed by another, and another. The Heinkel shuddered to the recoil of its own machine-guns as the gunners raked a fighter that sped past, revealing the graceful, elliptical curve of its wings. Held, feeling utterly naked, cowered in the cockpit behind the pilot and had a fleeting glimpse of a line of jagged holes appearing in the Spitfire's fuselage, just aft of the roundel. Then it was gone.

Held cursed himself for a coward; that would have made a brilliant shot, and he had missed it. Grey fingers of smoke filled the sky. Hazy fumes from the guns drifted through the Heinkel's cockpit, making his eyes water. Away to the left a Heinkel dropped out of formation, both engines pouring smoke. There was a sudden blinding flash as a Spitfire, its controls stiffened by the speed, smashed headlong into a second bomber. Two parachutes blossomed out from nowhere and hung there, tiny white splashes against the darker hues of the landscape below. Something – it was impossible to tell whether British or German – fell through the formation in flames, leaving an arrow-straight trail of oily black smoke. Then, suddenly, the Spitfires vanished as rapidly as they had come, heading back to their bases to refuel and rearm.

The bomber pilots closed up the gaps in their ranks

and the formation droned on towards its target. Held found that his heart was pounding, and that his breath was coming in short gasps. He had never dreamed that it would be like this. At headquarters, they had told him that the Tommies were finished, that they had no fighters left.

All over south-east England, from the Channel coast to London, the sky was filled with combat as the Spitfires and Hurricanes threw themselves on the *Luftwaffe* formations, breaking through the screens of escorting Messerschmitts time and again. The German fighter pilots, in fact, were having a hard time of it. Tied to the bomber groups by the invisible thread of the 'close escort' order, they were bounced time after time by British fighters, attacking from a higher altitude. The British tactics were simple: they would dive down, make one quick firing pass at a bomber, then continue to dive until they had gained sufficient speed to zoom rapidly back to altitude and repeat the process. Fighter Command was learning its lesson, and the German fighter pilots, forbidden to go after the speeding British fighters, watched helplessly as one bomber after another went down in flames.

The bomber formation to which Held's aircraft belonged was beginning its run-in to the target. In the cockpit of the Heinkel, the pilot chewed imperturbably on an unlit cigar butt, holding the aircraft on a steady course as it rode through the waves of flak that the London defences hurled at it. Behind the pilot, clutching his camera with one hand and the back of the pilot's seat with the other, Held strove to keep his balance, bracing his feet wide apart on the bucking metal floor. His legs ached as the Heinkel jolted with each shock wave from a nearby shell burst, and he wished there were a spare seat.

The cameraman winced as dirty tufts of smoke blossomed all around. Some of the explosions were so close that he could see the red flash of the burst and hear the crack above the roar of the bomber's engines. Metal splinters drummed like hail on the wings and fuselage, and he thought in sudden terror how thin the bomber's skin was. At any moment, a wicked red-hot piece of metal might rip through and penetrate his shrinking body, unprotected as it was by any armour plate.

Ahead, the smoke of old flak bursts mingled into a single towering cloud that resembled a thunderhead. The Heinkel bored on through it and Held smelled the reek of it. In the bomber's nose, the navigator/bomb aimer was peering through his sight and issuing a steady stream of instructions to the pilot, who was striving to hold the Heinkel steady. Held marvelled at the bomb aimer's calm voice.

A shell burst under the Heinkel with a wicked bang and the bomber leaped upwards on the shock wave. The pilot corrected it instantly and asked if everyone was all right. One by one, the crew members checked in, the ventral gunner reporting that the tailplane had collected some shrapnel holes.

A Heinkel on the edge of the formation blew up in a

great, slow explosion as a shell found its bomb load. Appalled, Held watched the debris cascade down towards the city, trailing streamers of fire. He resisted the temptation to film it: his orders expressly forbade the filming of damaged or destroyed German aircraft. He found that he was drenched in sweat, although it was a cold sweat of fear. He felt like screaming at the bomb aimer to get on with it. *Christus!* he thought, these fellows have to go through this hell day after day. Suddenly, he felt very small and superfluous, a cowardly interloper among a small band of gallant men.

'*Bomben los!*'

The Heinkel leaped buoyantly as its bombs cascaded from its belly and fell in a cluster towards the docks. Held breathed a prayer of relief as the pilot opened the throttles and put down the nose to gather speed, turning away from the hellish flak. Held pulled himself together and managed to film sticks of bombs falling from other aircraft, keeping his camera trained on the missiles until they disappeared into the smoke clouds below.

The Spitfire and Hurricane squadrons which had first engaged the enemy, their guns red-hot, out of fuel, riddled with holes, their pilots already exhausted, struggled back to their airfields to be feverishly rearmed and refuelled by the overworked ground crews in readiness for a fresh onslaught. For the retreating bombers of the first wave, however, there was to be no respite. The reserve squadrons of Nos. 11 and 12 Groups fell on them as they fled for the coast, and every available fighter was thrown into the battle.

For a split second, Held thought that the Hurricane was going to hit them. Before he had time to draw breath it grew from a tiny dot to a black, menacing shape that filled the windscreen. Then it was gone, zipping a few inches above the bomber's glazed nose.

There was a loud bang, a flash of flame and an icy blast of air screamed into the aircraft. Hot liquid spurted over Held's face, blinding him. Panic churned at his stomach and he dropped his camera, instinctively raising his hands to cover his eyes. It was a long second before he realised that he had not been hit. He staggered, clutching at the back of the pilot's seat to steady himself. With a sickening surge of horror, he realised that he was drenched in blood. In front of him, the pilot was slumped in his straps, his headless corpse pumping blood over the instrument panel and the remains of the windscreen.

Desperately, barely knowing what he was doing and fighting down his nausea, Held clawed his way forward and tore at the dead pilot's harness with one hand, grabbing the control column with the other as the Heinkel threatened to fall away in a spiral dive. Someone was shouting incoherently in his ear, tugging at the pilot's body. It was the navigator, his face white with terror.

Between them they managed to drag the pilot's body clear and dump it in an unceremonious heap on the cockpit catwalk. The navigator, thanking God that the pilot had allowed him to handle the controls and had given him rudimentary lessons in flying the Heinkel – a common practice in case of just such an emergency – hurled himself into the blood-spattered seat, planting his feet firmly on the rudder pedals and grasping the control wheel with both hands. The Heinkel had gone into a gentle, left-handed dive, but she came out sluggishly as the navigator applied opposite wheel and rudder, as the pilot had taught him, bringing the aircraft back to level flight once more.

Half a mile astern, Dickie Baird stood his black-painted Hurricane on its wingtip, pulling the fighter round in a tight turn on the Heinkel's tail. The bomber went into a shallow turn to the right, gaining speed, and Baird tightened his own turn still more, firing his twin cannon as the dark, twin-engined silhouette entered his sight. He saw his shells strike home on the bomber's port engine and punch large holes in the fuselage, just behind the upper gun position.

Not knowing what else to do, Held crouched down behind the pilot's seat, trying not to look at the corpse of the pilot. The shudder of gunfire jarred his teeth. A series of hammer-blows shook the aircraft and a chunk of metal tore away from the port engine cowling, followed by a thin streamer of smoke. The navigator reached over and punched the fire extinguisher button; the smoke trail turned white and died away. The engine continued to run, although the oil-pressure gauge climbed rapidly towards the danger mark.

The Hurricane flashed overhead and turned in again for a beam attack. The navigator turned the control wheel and applied hard rudder, trying to swing the bomber round so that the gunners would have a good field of fire. Held looked over his shoulder, seeing the strange black fighter come slanting in like an emissary from hell. The Heinkel's machine-guns chattered, then more hammer-blows sounded and Held saw a streak of fire, a trail left by a glowing shell, pass right through the fuselage, leaving two gaping holes.

The upper gunner suddenly dropped from his position, falling to his knees on the fuselage catwalk, his mouth wide open in a soundless scream as he tried to stuff his entrails back into his stomach with bloody hands. He swayed from side to side, face contorted in horror, then his bulging eyes lost their light and he collapsed face down.

Baird came arrowing in for a third attack, lining his fighter up carefully. There was no return fire; his last burst must have killed or wounded the enemy gunners. He closed in to fifty yards and jabbed his thumb down on the gun button, aiming for the bomber's starboard engine.

Only one cannon fired, and that too packed in after discharging only a few rounds. He pressed the button until his thumb hurt, yelling and swearing in frustration. The Heinkel steadied itself on a south-easterly heading, droning out over the Channel. It was as though its pilot knew that his pursuer was suddenly impotent.

Jürgen Held had resigned himself to the fact that he

was going to die. He felt utterly calm and detached, as though observing himself from the outside. He felt a vague sense of amazement. The shuddering, vibrating bomber, the howl of the slipstream through the remains of the canopy, the blood-spattered floor – all were part of a dream. None of this was really happening to him. In a second, he would wake up in the comfort of his room.

Then reality sliced at him brutally, like a knife, ripping away the curtain of illusion. Stark terror replaced it, clawing at his guts. Trembling and shivering in a bath of cold sweat, he looked around frantically, searching for the Hurricane.

A dark shadow fell across his face, startling him. The British fighter was sitting a few yards off the starboard wingtip, slightly higher up, a sinister black shadow against the sun. Then it peeled off and vanished, diving away towards the coast. Held closed his eyes, almost sick with relief. He was going to live. He sat down heavily on the metal floor of the cockpit and hugged his knees, rocking to and fro.

In front of him, the navigator-turned-pilot took a deep breath and looked at his instruments. Both engines were still running, although the port one was overheating badly. He had no idea how well the Heinkel would fly on one engine, and although he knew how to shut down the damaged motor, he decided to let it run and risk it bursting into flames. Every mile of Channel that crept beneath the bomber's wings meant a mile further from England, and if the worst came to the worst he and the Film Unit fellow could always bale out, preferably over land. Even if they came down in the sea, they would stand a reasonable chance of being picked up by the German air-sea rescue service. He took a firm grip on the control wheel, his heart leaping into his mouth every time the damaged engine missed a beat, and pointed the Heinkel's nose towards the spot where the promontory of Cap Gris Nez lay hidden behind the shallow curtain of haze that hung over the French coast.

A few minutes later, a young German gunner on the clifftops near Gris Nez suddenly pointed out over the Channel. 'Look,' he cried, 'there's another one!'

The NCO at his elbow, a veteran of the battles in Poland and Norway, took a bite out of a thick slice of sausage. 'All right,' he grunted, peering seawards, 'no need to get excited.'

The returning bombers had been coming in over the coast for a while now, many of them showing signs of battle damage. This one, flying low over the water, seemed to be in real trouble. It was a Heinkel, and one of its engines was streaming flame. It headed straight for the cliffs half a mile up the coast, pulling up at the last minute and clearing the tops with only a couple of metres to spare. An instant later, the burning engine blew up and the bomber went into a diving turn, shedding blazing fragments. Incredibly, it righted itself and hung poised for an endless second, tail down, before striking the ground with a concussion that the men in the emplacement felt clearly. Throwing out a cloud of debris, the bomber slewed to a stop in a field.

'Shall we go and help?' the young gunner asked eagerly.

'Looks like they've got enough,' the NCO told him. Troops were already hurrying to the scene, led by a motorcycle detachment. Some time later, one of the motorcycles came up and halted near the gun emplacement. The rider dismounted and came over, removing his goggles and coughing dust from his throat. His uniform was blackened by smoke from the burning aircraft.

'Got anything to drink?' he asked. The young gunner poured him some coffee. 'Bloody awful mess back there,' the motorcyclist said, sipping the hot liquid gratefully. 'Bodies all over the place.'

'Was anyone still alive?' the young gunner wanted to know, with a kind of morbid fascination. The motorcyclist nodded. 'Yes, there was one. Very strange, too. He must have literally walked out of the wreck. Nothing wrong with him, apart from some cuts and bruises. The weird thing was, he had a camera and was filming the wreck and the bodies. Kept shouting his mouth off about sending the film to Adolf so he could see what was really going on. Completely off his rocker, I'd say.'

His brow furrowed in puzzlement. 'Funny thing was, the fellow wasn't wearing any flying badges. Quite crazy, though. The Security Police have got hold of him now.

They'll probably lock him up or shoot him, or both. Well, thanks for the coffee. See you in England in a few days.'

They watched him depart. 'I wouldn't bank on it,' the NCO said moodily, staring at the thin white line of chalk cliffs that were just visible on the distant horizon.

# Chapter Thirteen

'It was damned bad luck, Dickie, that's all I can say.'

Baird snorted and stared at Armstrong, who was sitting on the wing of his Hurricane, munching an apple. The Fleet Air Arm pilot was still smarting over the loss of 'his' Heinkel, and took little comfort from the fact that his armourer had isolated the problem – it had been an electrical fault in the firing circuit, and the guns themselves had not been to blame – and had fixed it.

'You'll get another chance soon,' Kalinski assured him. The Pole had returned to duty two days earlier, the butt of a great deal of humour; half the hair on his scalp had been shaved off, and a large sticking plaster covered the spot where the enemy bullet had creased his head. Unlike his unfortunate gunner, Sergeant Burton, Kalinski had been very lucky, not just in the fact that he had just missed having his head blown off; he had kept on losing consciousness during the flight back from Holland, and had just managed to crash-land his Blenheim in a lucid moment. How he had not gone down in the sea, he would never know.

The pilot who had gone down into the sea, Flight Sergeant Van Berg, was also back, having rejoined the unit after a quick conversion course on Hurricanes. His gunner, Jordison, had gone off on one of the mysterious special courses that had already claimed his colleagues.

Armstrong had four black-painted, cannon-armed Hurricanes at his disposal now, the flight – it could not by any stretch of the imagination be called a squadron – being temporarily based at West Malling, a pleasant aerodrome just off the main London to Maidstone road. The adjacent village had plenty of character, with its old coaching inn, the Swan Hotel, and its attractive Norman church, St Mary's, whose squat tower was surmounted by a spire of later date. Just beyond the church was a manor house, which had been requisitioned as the Officers' Mess; the building was covered in ivy and there were magnificent gardens at front and rear. The manor house drive led to a sunken road, on the other side of which there was a long, narrow lake, the home of ducks, swans and moorhens. The house stood close to the site of a Benedictine abbey founded by Bishop Gundulf of Rochester; the abbey had been destroyed by fire, which had consumed most of the village, and the stones had been used to build the present house, which until recently had been the home of Anglican Benedictine nuns, who looked after elderly ladies.

The nuns and the elderly ladies had been moved elsewhere, to a place of greater safety, but they had left a legacy in the form of various rules and regulations that adorned the walls and which caused much merriment among the new tenants. One, in particular, warned that ladies could not be accepted unless they were capable of walking upstairs unaided.

It was all very English, and the peaceful scene had not been much disturbed by the arrival of the Royal Flying Corps at the nearby field in the First World War. Civil aviation had arrived in the 1930s, when the field became known as Maidstone Airport; then the RAF had taken over in June 1940, installing the Army Co-operation Westland Lysanders of No. 26 Squadron, soon followed by the Boulton Paul Defiants of No. 141 Squadron.

The Defiants had lasted barely a month, until a disastrous day in July when the squadron had been hacked to pieces over the Channel by Me 109s. Six Defiants were shot down, and the three survivors flew away to Prestwick in Scotland, never to return.

The War really came to West Malling in August, when the airfield was attacked seven times and considerable damage caused. On 3 September the aerodrome was attacked again and cratered by thirty bombs, causing the Lysanders to move hastily to Gatwick. The bomb craters had been filled in quickly, and three days after the attack

Armstrong's Hurricane flight moved in, with orders to intercept night bombers en route to London; but the pilots had soon found themselves involved in the daylight battle of 7 September, with nothing to show for it other than Baird's Heinkel, which he could only claim as damaged.

The day's fighting had been costly for both sides, with Fighter Command shooting down forty-one of the enemy but losing twenty-eight of their own. Between the Kentish coast and London, the harvest fields were strewn with the burning beacons of crashed aircraft, shattered mounds of aluminium eaten by petrol-fed fires. Here, in a wood, the torn branches concealed the compressed remains of a Spitfire, the pulped body of its 19-year-old pilot still strapped in the bloody cockpit; there, in a huge crater, a few shards of smoking metal were all that remained of a Dornier, which had dived straight in from a height of three miles, the explosion of its bomb load scattering the chalky soil over several fields.

There was no time, yet, to count the cost. The defenders licked their wounds and toiled feverishly to prepare themselves for the next round, their eyes on the southern sky. Dazed pilots threw themselves on the sun-baked ground and slept, the stink of cordite heavy in their nostrils; others crept quietly away, their stomachs knotted with reaction, not wishing their friends to see their bodies quivering with nausea at the thought of having to face the packs of Messerschmitts again, yet knowing that they would have to fly and fight as often as they had to, each time until the last. And beneath a pall of smoke London shook herself like an angry old dog and waited, tensing against the expected wail of sirens that would herald a fresh onslaught, as the sun began its long fall towards the western horizon.

At West Malling, as the evening wore on, Armstrong and his small band of pilots waited. They were still waiting when, at six o'clock, with the red ball of the sun about to be eclipsed by the turning earth, Baird spotted a lone figure cycling furiously towards them from the direction of the village. It was the newly promoted Flying Officer Briggs, the adjutant, who had come down from Bircham Newton to join them.

Briggs threw his bicycle down and handed Armstrong a slip of paper. 'Signal, sir,' he said breathlessly. 'Just come in.'

Armstrong read it in the fading light, then turned to face the others, his countenance grave.

'It's Cromwell,' he said. There was no need of explanation. They all knew what the code word meant, for they had been briefed to expect it. Cromwell: invasion imminent. The RAF and the Royal Navy were already at a high state of readiness, but the code word, issued by Headquarters Home Forces, would bring all troops in southern England to battle stations. Armstrong gazed at the spire of St Mary's church, and wondered whether its bells would peal tonight.

On the other side of the Channel, 200 bomber crews of *Luftflotte* 3 were preparing for the night's operations.

Again, Thameshaven and the London docks were to be the main objectives. The crews were assured that they would have no difficulty in locating their targets: all they had to do was to head for the fires started during the daytime raids, their glow clearly visible from the French coast.

*

*London, 8 September 1940: 01.00 Hours*

Looking down on London from 15,000 feet, Armstrong had never felt so helpless. The whole of the East End was a sea of flame, the lurid blood-red glare lighting up the clouds of smoke that obscured the tight-packed streets and alleys. Even as he watched, streams of incendiaries burst across the ground in flashes of fire, dropped by the raiders he could not see. And all that stood between London's torment and the bombers, discounting the anti-aircraft batteries which pumped thousands of shells into the sky but missed far more aircraft than they hit, were a few Bristol Blenheim night-fighters and four Hurricanes.

Armstrong brought the Hurricane round in a broad sweep around East London, keeping well clear of the main searchlight concentrations. Being shot down by his own side was a prospect he did not relish. He looked at the seething flames below, consuming homes and churches and friendly pubs, and thought of the Blue Bells and Phyllis, and a surge of rage went through him at the wanton destruction, at the very thought of foreign crews in their foreign bombers flying in *his* sky.

A sudden flurry of shellfire caught his attention, a twinkling of shell bursts flickering across the sky to the north, away from the bombers' main route, and he decided to investigate. He opened the throttle and climbed, taking the Hurricane up to 18,000 feet. Away on his right the moon, in its last quarter, was climbing laboriously into the eastern sky.

He strained his eyes, trying to work out the pattern of the anti-aircraft fire. The flashes seemed to be traversing the sky from north-west to south-east, converging on his own course. He turned onto a heading of 045 degrees, climbing hard over the Thames. Anti-aircraft fire was coming up thick and fast now, and the black-painted Hurricane rocked as shells burst dangerously close. Searchlights stabbed upwards, probing the night. Far ahead, a silvery midge was caught in one of the beams and other searchlights converged on it, trapping it in a spider's web of light. The midge began to twist and turn, frantically seeking an avenue of escape as shell after shell erupted around it. Then it flared briefly and began to fall, a glowing coal in the darkness, to be extinguished in a splash of red somewhere on the coast.

At least someone was on the ball, Armstrong thought as he continued climbing, pushing his vision to the limit in an effort to locate the elusive bombers. They must be all around him, but with the glare from the searchlights it was impossible to see a thing.

Suddenly, the Hurricane buffeted violently, shaken by

some unseen agent. Instinctively, Armstrong knew that he had flown through the turbulent slipstream of a large aircraft. It must have passed very close to him. He turned steeply to left and right, searching for the other machine and cursing the searchlights. There was no sign of it. He decided to take a chance and headed for the Thames estuary, hoping that the bomber was on its way home and that he would catch sight of it when London's glare fell astern and his full night vision returned.

A couple of minutes later, out of the comer of his eye, he had a vague impression of something fleeting across the moon. He turned, blinking to clear his eyes, careful not to look directly at the spot; it was much easier to use one's peripheral vision to locate something elusive under conditions such as these.

Excitement shot through him like a lance as two bright pinpoints of blue light appeared, a few hundred yards ahead and slightly to the left. He was looking at the exhaust flames of a twin-engined bomber, flying at the same height as himself. He dropped a couple of hundred feet and closed in, intent on attacking the enemy from underneath. He saw, now, that the raider was dragging twin vapour trails in its wake, and was surprised that he had not seen it sooner. He realised that the hot gases of the Hurricane's engine exhaust must also be forming a trail behind him; it would be clearly visible in the moonlight, the aircraft at his head presenting a target for the gunners on the ground.

The vapour streamed over his cockpit as he manoeuvred

carefully into position, the Hurricane giving little nervous twitches as it responded to his movement of the controls. Remembering the sight of the burning streets far below, he felt a terrible impulse to tear straight in to the attack, but resisted it; he knew that if he missed with his first burst, he might lose the target for good.

The bomber was recognisable now as a Dornier 17. He stalked it patiently, waiting until the range was down to a hundred yards. Then he opened fire.

There was the usual thudding recoil, the flashes from the muzzles of his guns as they sent several pounds of white-hot metal punching into the Dornier's belly. The vivid flashes of the exploding shells lit up the long, slender fuselage with its white-edged black crosses. The bomber shuddered violently and went into a steep, right-handed spiral dive. Red streaks lanced at the pursuing Hurricane from one of the enemy's gun positions, but the return fire was a long way wide of the mark.

Armstrong followed the bomber as it went down, the needle of the altimeter unwinding rapidly. He had no difficulty in keeping the Dornier in sight; its fuselage was glowing with some internal fire caused by his first burst. Red and white pyrotechnics showered from the bomber's cockpit as the crew tried to confuse him by firing a series of recognition flares, a ruse born of desperation that had no hope of succeeding.

At 4,000 feet the Dornier levelled out and turned towards the coast in a desperate attempt to get away. Its rear gunner was still blazing away wildly. Armstrong fired again, and saw orange flames burst from the bomber's port wing as his shells found a fuel tank. A moment later the Dornier went into a steep dive. It struck the sea just beyond the coast and bounced over the waves, each bounce marked by a splash of blazing fuel. Armstrong flew over the spot, then climbed back over the coast. He didn't think that any of the Dornier's crew had managed to bale out. Realising that he must have used up most of his ammunition in the combat – the ammunition drums held only 180 rounds – he set course for West Malling, touching down between the flarepath lights a few minutes later.

Baird was already back, and wearing a beaming smile; this time his cannon had worked, and he had bagged a Heinkel over the estuary. Kalinski, who came in shortly after Armstrong, had taken a shot at another Heinkel, but to his disgust he had lost it in the glare of searchlights; Van Berg, the last to land, had seen nothing at all during his patrol.

The attacks on London continued throughout the night, ceasing only at 04.30, and 448 civilians were killed along the nine miles of Thames waterfront, with many more injured. But no invasion came, even though there were plenty of scares; in one or two places the Local Defence Volunteers, exercising their initiative, blew up bridges to prevent the Germans getting across, while bells were rung in some villages on the Suffolk coast – a chain reaction in response to a warning buoy's bell offshore, set ringing by the accidental close passage of a fast destroyer.

In contrast to the onslaught of 7 September, the next day was relatively quiet, with desultory fighting in which the RAF lost four fighters and the *Luftwaffe* thirteen aircraft. But on 9 September the bombers returned, attacking Southampton and targets in the Thames estuary. A major raid on London by 200 bombers was broken up by fighters of Nos. 11 and 12 Groups, the latter now fully committed to the battle; but jettisoned bombs caused widespread damage in the suburbs, killing 412 people. The *Luftwaffe* lost twenty-five aircraft and the RAF seventeen.

On 11 September the Germans returned in strength, carrying out several co-ordinated attacks on London and selected airfields. West Malling was hit again, but Armstrong's fighter flight had departed, continuing to lead a nomadic existence; this time its destination was Speke, near Liverpool, and its mission was to guard the Rootes factory on the edge of the airport – engaged in vital aircraft production – against air attack. But the *Luftwaffe* seemed content to leave Speke alone, and although the Hurricanes were scrambled several times in vain attempts to intercept enemy bombers raiding Liverpool, their pilots spent most of their time fuming in frustration on the ground while the battle continued to rage elsewhere.

During the day's fighting, for the first time, the RAF suffered more heavily than the *Luftwaffe*, losing twenty-seven aircraft against the enemy's twenty-two. Again, it was the Hurricane squadrons that took the most punishment, losing nineteen aircraft with a further eight damaged.

On 12 and 13 September air operations were hampered by bad weather, the Germans losing eight aircraft in a series of sporadic small-scale raids and the RAF a solitary Hurricane. On the second day, Bomber Command switched the major part of its offensive to the Channel ports. Operation Sealion, the planned invasion of Britain, was due to take place on 15 September, but doubts were already being expressed in high German quarters that it would take place at all. Fighter Command's bitter struggle over southern England, and Bomber Command's parallel offensive against the ports, were having a combined effect, as stated in a signal to Berlin from HQ Navy Group West:

> *Interruptions caused by the enemy air forces, long-range artillery and light naval forces have, for the first time, assumed major significance. The harbours at Ostend, Dunkirk, Calais and Boulogne cannot be used as night anchorages for shipping because of the danger of English bombing and shelling. Units of the British fleet are now able to operate almost unmolested in the Channel. Owing to these difficulties further delays are expected in the assembly of the invasion fleet . . .*

The next day, Adolf Hitler issued a Supreme Command Directive postponing the launch of Operation Sealion until 17 September. Before that, on Sunday the 15th, London was again subjected to a ferocious assault as 200 bombers attacked the capital, the main raid coming in at noon.

In the underground operations of No. 11 Group, Air Vice-Marshal Keith Park looked at the status board; his last six fighter squadrons had just been ordered to take off and a further five were being sent to his aid by No. 12 Group, on the northern fringe of the battle.

Park turned to the man by his side, the most important visitor the Group had entertained, except for the King himself. An hour earlier, on an impulse, Winston Churchill, accompanied by his wife, had motored over to Uxbridge from his country home, Chequers, to watch the course of the battle from its nerve centre. In silence, he followed events from the raised controller's platform, looking down into the big room with its plotting table showing the battle situation. As fresh information came in from the radar stations and the Observer Corps, the coloured raid plots crept closer to London. On the wall opposite, a large illuminated board showed the battle state of every British fighter squadron in the Group's area: which ones were in reserve, which were airborne, which were in combat.

Churchill, who had been silent until now, turned to Park and asked how many reserve squadrons he had left.

'None,' the air vice-marshal replied bluntly. 'They are all engaging the enemy.'

Churchill knew precisely what that meant. If the Germans sent over a second wave of bombers immediately, the fighter squadrons would be on the ground, refuelling and rearming, and London would be at the enemy's mercy. But it was two hours before the second wave came, and by that time the squadrons of Fighter Command were ready for it. A total of 148 bombers got through to bomb the capital, but 56 were shot down and many more were damaged. One Dornier 17 pilot who got back reported that KG 3's airfield at Antwerp seemed to be littered with wrecks. There were Dorniers with collapsed undercarriages, Dorniers with shattered cockpits, Dorniers with half their tails shot away. Ground crews stared with horrified eyes as bullet-riddled aircraft taxied in. Not until this moment had they begun to have an inkling of the disaster that had befallen the *Luftwaffe* on the other side of the Channel.

Fighter Command had come close to extinction, but now the tide was beginning to turn in its favour. Meanwhile, Bomber Command continued its attacks on the invasion ports. They were easy to find, but they were far from easy to attack. Flak was plentiful and losses were heavy. The anti-aircraft defences were particularly strong around Antwerp, and it was while attacking this target on the night of 15 September that an 18-year-old air gunner, Sergeant John Hannah, one of the crew of a Handley Page Hampden of No. 83 Squadron, performed an act of gallantry that earned him a Victoria Cross, and exemplified the courage of all the bomber crews. The citation told the story:

*On the night of 15 September 1940, Sergeant Hannah was the wireless operator/air gunner in an aircraft engaged in a successful attack on an enemy barge concentration at Antwerp. It was then subjected to intense anti-aircraft fire and received a direct hit from a projectile of an explosive and incendiary nature, which apparently burst inside the bomb compartment. A fire started which quickly enveloped the wireless operator's and rear gunner's cockpits, and as both the port and starboard petrol tanks had been pierced there was a grave risk of fire spreading. Sergeant Hannah forced his way through to obtain two extinguishers and discovered that the rear gunner had had to leave the aircraft. He could have acted likewise, through the bottom escape hatch or forward through the navigator's hatch, but remained and fought the fire for ten minutes with the extinguishers, beating the flames with his log book when these were empty.*

*During this time thousands of rounds of ammunition exploded in all directions and he was almost blinded by the intense heat and fumes, but had the presence of mind to obtain relief by turning on his oxygen supply. Air admitted through the large holes caused by the projectile made the bomb compartment an inferno and all the aluminium sheet metal on the floor of this airman's cockpit was melted away, leaving only the cross bearers. Working under these conditions, which caused burns to his face and eyes, Sergeant Hannah succeeded in extinguishing the fire. He then crawled forward, ascertained that the navigator had left the aircraft, and passed the latter's log and maps to the pilot.*

*This airman displayed courage, coolness and devotion to duty of the highest order and by his action in remaining and successfully extinguishing the fire under conditions of the greatest danger and difficulty, enabled the pilot to bring the aircraft to its base.*

The next morning, the German Naval War Staff reported that:

> *In Antwerp considerable casualties have been inflicted on transports. Five transport steamers in the port have been heavily damaged . . . one barge has been sunk, two cranes destroyed, an ammunition train has blown up, and several sheds are burning.*

For the Germans, there was worse to come. On the night of 16 September, only hours before the crucial German Supreme Command conference that was to decide whether or not the invasion was to take place, a force of British bombers surprised a strong concentration of enemy landing craft in the open sea off Boulogne, engaged in an invasion training exercise. Several barges and two transports were sunk, with heavy loss of life. German bodies, washed up on the English coast some days later, gave rise to rumours that an invasion had actually been attempted.

On that same night the RAF also struck at the whole coastal area between Antwerp and Le Havre, prompting the German Naval Staff to report in the morning that:

> *. . . The RAF are still by no means defeated; on the contrary, they are showing increasing activity in their attacks on the Channel ports and in their mounting interference with the assembly movements.*

The statement was underlined by Bomber Command on the night of 17 September, when, under a half moon, every available aircraft – 197 of them – pounded the Channel ports and caused the biggest damage so far to the invasion fleet. Eighty-four barges were sunk or damaged at Dunkirk alone, while elsewhere a large ammunition dump was blown up, a supply depot burned out and several steamers and MTBs sunk. The next day, the Naval Staff report made gloomy reading:

> *The very severe bombing, together with bombardment by naval guns across the Channel, makes it necessary to disperse the naval and transport vessels already concentrated on the Channel and to stop further movement of shipping to the invasion ports. Otherwise, with energetic enemy action such casualties will occur in the course of time that the execution of the operation on the scale previously envisaged will in any case be problematic.*

On Thursday, 19 September, four days after the great air battle over London and southern England that would henceforth be marked as Battle of Britain Day, Adolf Hitler ordered the invasion forces in the Channel ports to be dispersed so that 'the loss of shipping space caused by enemy air attacks may be reduced to a minimum'. Operation Sealion had been postponed indefinitely.

# Chapter Fourteen

The twenty Me 109s came in high and fast, flying in five sections of four and keeping a tight formation. Four and a half miles below, London sprawled untidily, wreathed in smoke and tendrils of cloud.

Looking ahead, *Oberleutnant* Hans Lehmann, recently promoted, could see filmy vapour trails twisting across the sky. The German fighters were airborne with a vengeance today, mounting large-scale offensive sweeps over south-east England. These were the *Luftwaffe's* new tactics: while the bombers restricted their operations to night raids the fighters would speed into English skies by day, hit hard at the RAF squadrons that rose to meet them, and withdraw in good order.

Lehmann's pilots, however, had orders to avoid battle at all costs. Each Messerschmitt was weighed down by a 250-kg bomb, fitted on a special shackle under its belly, and in that condition the fighters were in no position to tangle with the Spitfires and Hurricanes. The order to modify Special Group 210's single-engined fighters in this way had been received a few days earlier, following a series of disastrous losses suffered by the unit's twin-engined Me 110s, and Lehmann had been given the task of proving the concept operationally.

It ought to work, he reassured himself, as long as they could avoid the British fighters as they approached the target. Once free of their bombs, they could fight their way out if they had to. But at this altitude, the risk of interception was low; most of the battles so far had taken place much lower down, and in any case the Tommies would be preoccupied with the fighters that had gone in earlier.

It was the first day of October, and much had happened since the *Luftwaffe* had been mauled over London a fortnight earlier. For a while, the Germans had persevered in their efforts to attack British targets by daylight using conventional bombers, taking advantage of showery weather and substantial cloud cover, but three further disasters had persuaded them that further operations of this kind were futile. On 18 September, a force of Junkers 88s attacking oil targets in the Thames estuary had been intercepted by a strong force of fighters, losing nine bombers in just three minutes; on the 27th, during renewed fine weather, attacks on London and Bristol had cost the *Luftwaffe* fifty-five aircraft; and another forty-eight had gone down on the 30th, when Fighter Command had defeated attacks on London and the Westland Aircraft factory at Yeovil.

The fifteen days of air fighting since mid-September had cost the *Luftwaffe* 210 bombers and fighters; the RAF had lost 122 Hurricanes and Spitfires, about a quarter of them in the big battles of the 27th.

For the first time, Lehmann had heard German pilots openly admitting that they were longing for a transfer to a quieter sector. Such comments, had, of course, been dealt with sharply, but the sentiment was there. Aircrews who, only a few weeks earlier, had been assured of a quick victory, had now lost faith in their leaders. Morale was at a low ebb.

Lehmann knew the reason for the urgency with which Special Group 210 had been ordered to convert all its aircraft to carry bombs. On the night of 23 September, RAF Bomber Command had sent over 130 aircraft to attack Berlin. For three hours, the British bombers had droned over the German capital. The news of the raid had been hushed up, of course, and Lehmann had only found out about it because Falcke, his wingman, had been enjoying a couple of days' well-deserved leave in the city when the bombs fell. Falcke had been shaken by the attack, which was on a far greater scale than Berlin had so far experienced. There was unrest among the workers of Moabit, the industrial quarter of the city where many of the bombs had apparently fallen.

Quietly, Lehmann had told Falcke not to voice his experiences to anyone else. There were inherent dangers in such talk.

Over the radio, Lehmann warned his pilots to stand by. Anti-aircraft shell bursts were beginning to stain the air underneath the Messerschmitt formation; at the moment the fighter-bombers were out of range, but soon they would have to dive through the barrage towards their target.

Lehmann had no fears that they might miss the target: it was the city of London itself. Lehmann didn't much care where the bombs fell, as long as they fell close together. Wherever they exploded, ten tons of explosives going off in close proximity were going to cause a lot of damage.

He had selected Westminster Bridge as his aiming point. He picked it out with some difficulty, for the downward view was becoming obscured by drifting smoke from the flak bursts, and watched it disappear under his left wing. He flew on, straight and level, until the bridge – looking like a tiny thread crossing the Thames – reappeared behind the trailing edge, then he turned the 109 over on its back and plummeted vertically down towards it, seeing the sprawling panorama below expand beyond the shimmering disc of his propeller.

Under the weight of its bomb the 109 dropped like a stone, its engine howling, shuddering and buffeting as the speed built up. Lehmann grimly held on to the control column with both hands, watching the needles of the altimeter and the air speed indicator moving across their dials with frightening speed, the former unwinding as the streets of London flew up to meet the Messerschmitt. Brown stains of flak bursts whizzed past the cockpit as the 109 continued its downward plunge at 700 k.p.h.

The altimeter showed 1,500 metres. Lehmann pressed the bomb release trigger and felt a thump as the missile dropped away, then – very gently, for he was afraid the wings might tear away – he began to ease the Messerschmitt out of its dive. He felt the force of gravity clawing at his cheeks as the 109's nose laboriously began to rise, and a grey veil slid over his eyes as the blood drained from his head. Dimly, through a state verging on loss of consciousness – a full blackout – he heard the aircraft emitting tortured noises. Then his vision cleared and he was racing across London at phenomenal speed, surrounded by smoke trails and shell bursts, whistling past a forest of barrage balloon cables that had suddenly appeared from nowhere.

He pulled back on the stick, using his forward speed to take the 109 into a rocketing climb that quickly took him clear of the worst of the ground fire. He turned and headed for the coast, looking back as he did so, and was gratified to see the other 109s shooting up out of the smoke like silvery bullets. Below them, he could see the flashes of their bomb bursts, straddling both banks of the Thames, then London faded astern.

High over the coast he throttled back, reducing speed to let the others catch up. One by one the other pilots checked in over the radio: everyone had got through safely. In ragged formation, they headed out over the Channel. They had not seen a single British fighter. The experiment had been a complete success.

The tactics continued to work during the next few days, during which the weather conditions varied considerably: spells of fine weather would alternate with cloud and showers. Lehmann, whose pilots operated over London and the English Channel ports almost every day, modified his fighter-bomber tactics as they gained experience. He worked out that it was better to approach the target in a long stream, so that each pilot could keep an eye on the tail of the aircraft ahead, and make a shallow diving attack at an angle of about forty-five degrees.

The bomb-armed Me 109s bore charmed lives; so far, none had been shot down, although a few had returned to base with flak damage. The Junkers 88 squadrons, on the other hand, which were still trying to attack aircraft factories, continued to take losses; on 7 October, seven Ju 88s were shot down in another attempted raid on the Westland Aircraft factory.

On 12 October, a senior *Luftwaffe* staff officer visited Special Group 210's base at Calais-Marck and ordered the squadron commanders to assemble in the operations room. There, without preamble, he read out a directive that had just been issued by HQ in Berlin: 'The Führer has decided that from now until the spring, preparations for Sealion shall be continued solely for the purpose of maintaining political and military pressure on England. Should the invasion be reconsidered in the spring or early summer of 1941, orders for a renewal of operational readiness will be issued later. In the meantime military conditions for a later invasion are to be improved.'

So that's it, Lehmann thought as he walked away from the operations room afterwards. There won't be an invasion. The Tommies have won. Hitler's decision made the prospect of further operations over the British Isles by day seem futile; the night-bombers were doing far more damage. After all, they carried more bombs and they had the range to attack targets all over Britain, even in Northern Ireland. In fact, Lehmann half expected to receive orders to resume normal fighter operations; but such orders never arrived. The fighter-bomber attacks were to continue.

Three days later, Special Group 210's luck ran out.

After a day of almost continuous rain, Tuesday, 15 October, was fair. This was to be a maximum effort: while Lehmann's bomb-carrying 109s attacked London, other Me 109 groups were to strafe enemy airfields in south-east England in the hope of taking Fighter Command by surprise. It was their bad luck that Fighter Command had four Spitfire and Hurricane squadrons airborne when the attack came in, and that the two Spitfire squadrons, alerted by the sector controllers that what appeared to be a fighter formation was assembling over Calais, had climbed to nearly 30,000 feet in readiness to meet the raiders.

The Germans never saw the RAF fighters until the latter were upon them. The first indication Lehmann had of danger was a frantic cry of alarm from the rearmost pilot of the Me 109 stream, a high-pitched note of terror that was abruptly cut off. In a single pass, the Spitfires sent three Me 109s flaming towards the Thames estuary, continuing their dive and zooming up for another firing pass.

Urgently, Lehmann ordered his pilots to jettison their bombs. A shower of missiles dropped away, curving towards Whitstable Bay and the Isle of Sheppey. As soon as the bombs fell from their shackles the pilots took violent evasive action, twisting away from the British fighters that seemed to be everywhere.

Lehmann made a head-on attack on a Spitfire, his cannon and machine guns thumping. There was no time to see if he had hit the mark, for the next instant the Tommy was streaking just above him, an indistinct blur that emitted a brief shriek of engine noise. Tracer passed over Lehmann's left wing and he broke hard in the opposite direction, craning his neck to see four Spitfires on his tail, queueing up for a shot at him.

He pushed the stick forward and dived away at full speed, maintaining the dive until he was almost at ground level. The 109 shuddered and vibrated alarmingly, and in a detached way he wondered if this was really it, if the wings, overstressed by the dive-bombing operations, were really going to come off this time. But the wings stayed where they were, and Lehmann, still pursued by two Spitfires, headed flat out for the coast, hedge-hopping over houses, standing the 109 on a wingtip as he tore around the edges of hills and woods. He knew that his only chance of escape was to stay low and fast, manoeuvring with all the flying skill at his disposal. The two Spitfires were still behind him, less than a hundred metres away, and if he tried to climb or to turn and fight one or the other would nail him.

He roared over Dover, jinking between the cables of the balloon barrage and saying a prayer of thanks that the flak had not opened up, presumably for fear of hitting the pursuing fighters. The wavetops were flashing by beneath his wings now, and he ducked involuntarily as bullets kicked up splashes a few feet in front of the Messerschmitt's nose. Sweat was pouring into his eyes. He risked another glance behind, and was relieved to see that only one Spitfire was still with him.

Every kilometre was bringing him closer to the French coast, and survival. He could see Cap Gris Nez now, a welcome sight, for his fuel was running low. The Tommy must be in a similar state, he thought; at any moment, the Spitfire pilot would be forced to break off the action and run for home. There had been isolated cases of British fighters pursuing German aircraft into France, but not many. Lehmann felt sure that the RAF fighter pilots had orders not to put their precious aircraft at risk in this way.

He glanced back again, and saw the Spitfire starting to turn away in a climb, a black puff of smoke breaking from its exhaust as the pilot reduced speed. Without even thinking, Lehmann whipped his Messerschmitt round in a tight turn, rolling out and heading straight for the other aircraft.

The RAF pilot had not anticipated such a move, and paid for his lack of foresight at the hands of his experienced German adversary. Lehmann fired a single burst, watching his strikes spatter the Spitfire's cockpit area, and almost collided with the British fighter as its nose reared up abruptly. It hung there for a moment, its propeller clawing the air, then tipped over and plunged into the sea in a great flurry of foam. Lehmann circled the spot once, seeing a few bits of wreckage bob to the surface, then made for his home airfield. He felt no elation in having shot down the Spitfire, just a sense of utter weariness. He was soaked in sweat from head to toe, and he realised with something akin to horror that the hand that held the Messerschmitt's control column was trembling violently. The more he tried to control the sensation, the worse it got.

On an impulse, he turned his oxygen to 'full' and took several deep breaths. Almost immediately he felt calmer, and his hand became steadier. It was not a moment too soon, for Calais-Marck airfield was dead ahead.

Lehmann went straight in to land, slotting in between other Messerschmitts that were on the approach. He had a sense of foreboding as he taxied in, and not long afterwards he knew that it was justified. Seven of his Messerschmitts were missing, and one of them was Falcke's.

Lehmann had no means of knowing it then, but Falcke was still very much alive. Seeing Lehmann's predicament, the wingman had tried to assist him by attacking the Spitfires that were in pursuit. As to what had happened after that, he was by no means certain; he recalled feeling a massive concussion, and the next thing he knew he had been floating down towards Kent on the end of his parachute, with a grandstand view of the air battle that raged around him.

It had not been a comfortable feeling, for the air stank of cordite and aircraft whistled past, sometimes dangerously close. But as he drifted closer to the ground the roar of battle gradually died away and the reality of his situation suddenly hit him. He was going down into captivity, and how long that captivity might last he had no idea. It might be weeks, he thought, even months before the Tommies were compelled to give up. The prospect did not appeal to him.

He landed heavily in the main street of a little village just outside Maidstone, twisting an ankle and bruising his shoulder badly. He managed to free himself from his parachute harness and, getting painfully to his knees, began to gather in the folds of parachute material.

## THE INTRUDERS

A shadow fell across him. He looked up and saw a very large woman standing over him. She wore a floral pinafore, her face was angrily red and determined, and she was brandishing a rolling pin. Falcke smiled weakly and, most wisely, decided to surrender.

# Chapter Fifteen

*Three quotes:*

*I walked past Buckingham Palace where the bomb damage is being repaired, and past Queen Anne's Mansions, hit four or five times, and Westminster and the House of Commons, both damaged. After this the War Office, which had a big bomb. From here past Trafalgar Square, where there are numerous sandbagged pillboxes and barbed wire entanglements, and to Albemarle Street, where two buildings are a heap of ruins. Dover Street has a dent in it where a bomb demolished two or three buildings next to Batt's Hotel. Piccadilly Arcade is blocked up completely at one end. Saville Row is fairly battered to pieces; all the glass is out in Bond Street and Regent Street. Not a shop in Conduit Street has any glass in it. And so on back along Oxford Street, where John Lewis is a burnt-out ruin and Selfridge's huge plate-glass windows have been shattered. Nevertheless, I look at the ruin of the West End with satisfaction, for it marks another of those famous German mistakes. Had they continued to batter the*

*East End and kill and destroy among the slums, there would certainly
have been great discontent. As it is, the only complaint the poor people
have is that government assistance to the homeless and the provision
of deep shelters are not being attended to with necessary promptness.*

    *Raymond Lee, United States
Military Attaché, London: Letter
to his Wife.*

*

*The night raids are continuing to do, I think, substantial damage
and the day raids have dealt most serious blows to Bristol,
Southampton and Liverpool. Production is definitely falling, regard-
less of what reports you may be getting, and with transportation
smashed up the way it is, the present production output will continue
to fall. My own feeling is that the British are in a bad way. Bombers
have got through in the daytime on the last three days and on four
occasions today substantial numbers of German planes have flown
over London and have done some daylight bombing.*

    *I cannot impress upon you strongly enough my complete lack of
confidence in the entire British conduct of this war. I was delighted
to see that the President said he was not going to enter the war,
because to enter this war, imagining for a minute that the English
have anything to offer in the line of leadership or productive capacity
in industry that could be of the slightest value to us, would be a
complete misapprehension.*

    *United States Ambassador Joseph
Kennedy to the Secretary of
State, Washington.*

\*

*What a complete asshole!*
*An American fighter pilot*
*serving in the RAF, on learning*
*of Ambassador Kennedy's*
*comments.*

\*

She was a beautiful aircraft. Every line of her exuded strength and power, from the odd-looking forked aerial at her nose to the upswept tailplane. On either side of the cockpit were the engines that would hurl her through the sky at over 300 m.p.h.: the big Bristol Hercules fourteen-cylinder radials, each producing 1,560 horsepower for take-off.

Her armament was staggering: four 20-mm Hispano cannon in the nose, their long barrels running under the cockpit floor, and six .303 Browning machine guns in the wings. The cannon were fed by ammunition drums, each containing sixty shells, and the machine guns had 1,000 rounds per gun.

The pilot had an excellent view from the cockpit, his face close to a sloping armoured windscreen, with perspex panels on either side and in the roof. No longer would there be any craning and peering to see out, half-blinded by the reflected light of the instruments, as had been the case in the Blenheim. The pilot entered the cockpit by means of a hatch set in the floor, cleverly balanced so that when it was unlocked in flight it pivoted around its mid-point and provided a windshield to assist escape in an emergency. In that event, the pilot pulled a lever to collapse the back of his seat, grasped a pair of handrails set above the forward hatch, pulled himself out over the front spar where it ran through the fuselage, and dropped out.

Behind the cockpit, armour-plated doors gave way to a catwalk leading to the observer's position. He sat under a small perspex cupola on a seat that could be swivelled right round to give easy access to the massive breeches of the four cannon, for part of his job was to reload the guns with spare spring-loaded ammunition drums, clipped into racks on the sides of the fuselage. He had his own entry and exit hatch, and for him getting out in an emergency would require fewer gymnastics than the pilot would have to perform.

The name of the powerful fighting machine was the Bristol Beaufighter, and she carried a device that was about to make life hard and costly for the German night-bombers. The Beaufighter crews called it simply 'the Box' or 'the Thing'. It was more properly known as Air Interception Radar Mk IV.

This was the aircraft, and the equipment, with which the Intruder Squadron was about to go to war. Gone were the days of the cannon-armed Hurricanes, of the hit-or-miss tactics of night interception. The Box would guide the night fighter to within striking distance of its target, and after that it would be up to the eyesight of the pilot, his skill at getting into a good firing position, and the amount of metal he could unleash at the touch of a button.

Armstrong's Intruder Squadron was a squadron in reality now, with nine Beaufighters, but it would not be operating over the continent for the foreseeable future; the Box was far too secret to risk its falling into enemy hands. What remained of the original 'firm' had come together once more: Armstrong and Kershaw leading the team, followed by Baird and Copeland, Kalinski and a new crew member called Trevarrow, and Van Berg and Jordison. The gunners were back from their mysterious course, except that the courses were no longer mysterious and the men were gunners no more; the brevet they wore bore the letters 'RO', which stood for Radio Observer. The five new crews, all former Blenheim men, seemed professional enough, and were clearly delighted with the 'Beau'.

It was not an aircraft, though, which readily forgave mistakes on the part of the pilot, and it was unstable when carrying a full load of ammunition, with a tendency to go into a dive or climb more steeply than was normal. Flying it needed an enormous amount of concentration, and there were horrifying stories of Beaufighters that had suddenly lost flying speed while coming in to land and spun into the ground. Armstrong, who had realised that the Beaufighter had a problem the first time he flew one, made sure that all his pilots – all of whom were used to the comparatively docile Blenheim – were fully aware of its unstable tendencies. The manufacturers were investigating the problem, and there were plans to fit a larger tail on later aircraft.

As for the Box, its workings had remained almost a complete mystery to him until the day he arranged a flight in an AI-equipped Blenheim so that Kershaw could explain the whole thing to him.

'It works just like a sound echo,' the RO told him earlier, as they examined an as yet inert AI set that had been set up in a building at West Malling, where the squadron was once again based. 'If you shout across a valley, your voice's sound waves hit the far side and bounce back across to be picked up by your ears. Or, if you like, it operates on the bat principle. A bat lets out a series of high-pitched squeaks which reflect back from an insect and enable the bat to home in on it. The night fighter's AI transmits radio waves, and if they hit anything they return to the fighter as an echo.'

'And presumably you can tell the distance of whatever it is they hit by the time it takes them to travel back,' Armstrong said, with a sudden flash of insight. Kershaw looked at him with the pleased expression of a teacher who had just discovered a spark of intelligence in an unusually dim pupil.

'That's right, sir. Now I'll show you how the thing

works.' He switched on the set, which emitted a low buzzing sound. A luminous green line appeared on its two cathode ray tubes, horizontal on one tube and vertical on the other.

'These are what we call the time traces,' Kershaw explained. Armstrong nodded sagely, not having the faintest idea what the RO meant. He was enlightened a moment later, when Kershaw twiddled a knob on the set and some little diamonds of light appeared, straddling the luminous lines.

'Those represent the echoes from the target, or 'blips' as they are better known. The distance of a blip from one end of the trace tells you the range of the target from the transmitter, and its position in relation to the trace shows its bearing. That's on this tube here, the one with the vertical line. It's called the azimuth tube. The elevation tube, with the horizontal trace, shows whether the target is above or below.'

'Astonishing,' Armstrong said. 'It looks simple enough, but I expect you have to do an awful lot of knob-twiddling. By the way, what's that thing that looks like a Christmas tree?' He pointed to a triangle of light, etched in green, attached to the base of the time trace. Kershaw grinned.

'That's exactly what we call it,' he said. 'It's the echo from the ground. The lower you fly, the bigger it gets, until at about six hundred feet it blots out the entire tube.'

'So why isn't it doing that now?' Armstrong wanted to know. 'After all, we're on the ground, aren't we?'

Kershaw looked at him reproachfully, all the pilot's earlier brownie points having just flown out of the window. 'This is a *synthetic* trainer, sir. The boffins from the Telecommunications Research Establishment fixed it up. They can do all sorts of wizardry,' he added rather lamely, not really knowing himself how the necessary information had been fed into the training device.

'Well, let's hope the real thing works,' Armstrong said. Kershaw looked slightly uncomfortable.

'It works all right,' he said, 'but the picture's nothing like as clear. You get interference, like the background noise on a radio set, and it shows up on the screen. Grass, we call it. And then there's something called squint, which can make the blip swing about a bit as you get close to the target.'

'Oh, well, anything's got to be an improvement,' Armstrong said reassuringly, recalling long hours of fruitless chases in the night sky over Merseyside. When Kershaw demonstrated the AI equipment in the air later on, however, he was not so sure.

Kalinski was flying the Blenheim, and an Airspeed Oxford was acting as the target aircraft. Armstrong crouched uncomfortably in the dark recess of the fuselage next to Kershaw, who was peering into the IA set's visor and issuing a stream of instructions to the pilot. As it was broad daylight, Kalinski had a clear view of the target aircraft. Armstrong, plugged into a spare intercom socket, listened intently to the proceedings. At length, Kershaw pronounced confidently that the target was dead ahead at 2,000 feet, 400 feet higher up.

'Okay,' Kalinski said. 'Come up front and take a look.'

They both went forward and peered up through the Blenheim's perspex nose panels at where the target was supposed to be. There was no sign of it. Kalinski obligingly dived a little, and then they saw the Oxford; it was 300 feet lower down.

'Oh, hell,' Kershaw said miserably. 'It's that bloody squint again.'

'Well, apart from that you got the range and position right,' Armstrong said. 'Any pilot would have been able to see the target on a good night. It's all a matter of practice, I reckon.'

And practice they did, first by day and then by night; and gradually, as the ROs got used to the foibles of the AI equipment, they learned to master it, or at least to come to terms with it. Pilots and observers learned, too, how to anticipate each other's moves and reactions so that they formed a fluid team. And, armed with a new confidence and an eagerness to get into the night battle, Armstrong declared his squadron operationally ready early in November.

By this time the nucleus of an effective night-fighter force was on place, with six squadrons now armed with the Beaufighter. The day of the slow old Blenheim as a night-fighter was over, although no one could take away from it the fact that it was a Blenheim of the Fighter

Interception Unit at Ford that, on the night of 23 July 1940, had made the first AI-assisted kill in history, shooting down a Dornier 17 off the Sussex coast while carrying out trials with the new equipment. The Dornier's four-man crew, all wounded in the attack, had nevertheless survived the experience and had been rescued.

The first Beaufighter kill had been scored on the night of 25 October, when the crew of a No. 219 Squadron aircraft from Catterick, in North Yorkshire, had shot down a Dornier off the north-east coast, but that had not been a radar interception; that honour still waited to be claimed, and a keen rivalry was beginning to develop among the squadrons to see which crew would be lucky.

The optimism was high; but on one November night the British public were made brutally aware that the German night-bombers still held the upper hand, a fact that the people of London, Merseyside and the towns on the Channel coast already knew to their cost. At 20.00 hours on the 14th, two squadrons of Heinkel He 111H-3 bombers roared off into the darkness from their base at Vannes, in Brittany. They crossed the Channel and droned high over the darkened south of England, heading towards their target in the Midlands. Behind them, from a powerful transmitter on the French coast, a radio beam lanced out into the night, forming an invisible road in the sky for the aircraft. A steady signal in the pilot's headphones meant that he was on course; dots or dashes meant that he was straying to left or right.

Each bomber was equipped with a special radio receiver known simply as 'X-Apparatus'. A signal, automatically triggered by a second beam cutting across the first at an angle from another radio transmitter, indicated that the bomber was now ten miles from the target. As soon as the signal was received, each radio operator pressed a switch, starting up a clock on his instrument panel. Five miles further on, in response to a signal from a third beam, the radio operator pressed the switch again, stopping the first pointer and starting a second.

It was now up to the pilot to hold the bomber steady on the final run-in to the target. Apart from opening the bomb doors, that was all he had to do; everything else was automatic. When the second pointer on the radio operator's clock became superimposed on the first, it triggered the electrical bomb release circuit and the bomb load fell away.

On this November night, the target was the lovely cathedral city of Coventry, earmarked by *Luftwaffe* Intelligence as an important munitions centre and therefore a legitimate military target. During the hours that followed, 450 German bombers, guided by the fires started by the pathfinding Heinkels of *Kampfgruppe* 100, dropped 500 tons of high explosive and 30 tons of incendiary bombs into the expanding sea of flame below. When the last wave of bombers droned away in the early hours of 15 November, the heart of Coventry, together with its beautiful fourteenth-century cathedral, had ceased to exist.

Five hundred and fifty-four of Coventry's citizens were dead, and 865 seriously injured. Fighter Command had flown 125 sorties, and its pilots had sighted only 7 bombers out of the hundreds that were airborne over England that night. None of the bombers sighted had been shot down by fighters, although Anti-Aircraft Command claimed a couple destroyed.

The very next day, Air Chief Marshal Sir Hugh Dowding, whose shoulders had borne the crushing burden of directing Fighter Command during the critical summer weeks, received a telephone call from the Secretary of State for Air, informing him that he was to be replaced at once . . .

Armstrong and several of his crews had been airborne from West Malling that night, patrolling No. 11 Group's sector, but the track followed by the German bombers heading to and from Coventry had been a long way to the west, over No. 10 Group's territory, and they had seen nothing. Other night-fighter crews, however, returned with frustrating stories of lost contacts, of AI sets that overheated and blew up, of big, bright 'blips' that suddenly shot away at incredible speed as the fighter closed with them. Morale was beginning to suffer, and no one knew quite what to do about it except continue to practise, and search for the elusive enemy, and practise some more.

Then, one night, the spectre of bad luck was banished. It happened on 20 November, when a radio operator called Sergeant Phillipson steered his pilot towards an enemy aircraft that was being followed by a concentration of searchlights. After a long chase the pilot saw the dark silhouette of the enemy, and shot the aircraft down. It was a Junkers 88.

The Beaufighter pilot was a flight commander with No. 604 Squadron at Middle Wallop. Armstrong had met him several times; he was a calm, unruffled man, a master of his trade and an excellent pilot. His name was John Cunningham, and in the months that followed he was to take the lead in the war against the night-bomber.

RAF Intelligence knew all about the special 'pathfinder' Heinkels of *Kampfgruppe* 100, and the night-fighters' main effort was directed against them. It was the *Luftwaffe's* choice of targets that gave the night-fighter crews their chance: their earlier attacks on London had meant that the bombers had only to spend a relatively short time in hostile air space before flying away across the Channel, but attacks on targets in the Midlands presented them with a different and more hazardous situation. After crossing the wide part of the Channel, and making land-fall between the Needles and Portland Bill, they had to cross a considerable stretch of blacked-out England before reaching the target area. In order to make an accurate landfall, the Heinkel crews tended to cross the seventy miles of Channel while it was still light, reaching the English coast at dusk, their navigators fixing the aircraft's position before making the long run across country.

The night-fighters adopted counter-tactics of their own,

patrolling over the Channel at low level and down-light in the hope of sighting the Germans against the afterglow of the sunset. The bombers could then be stalked visually or by AI until it was dark enough to make an attack.

The dusk patrol technique worked, and soon *Kampfgruppe* 100's Heinkels began to suffer. It was John Cunningham who got the first of them, fifty miles out to sea south of Lulworth. Hitting it with a storm of fire in its bomb bay, he saw it explode in an enormous display of cascading flares and incendiaries, the blazing wreck plunging into the cloud below.

But the Germans still had some tricks up their sleeve, as Kalinski discovered a few nights later as he patrolled the Thames estuary. He and his operator, Sergeant Trevarrow, had been flying for half an hour when the sector controller's urgent voice crackled in their headphones.

'There's a bandit approaching you. Turn onto zero-one-zero and flash your weapon.'

Kalinski swung the Beaufighter into the turn. Behind him, Trevarrow, face pressed against the visor, stared at the cathode ray tubes. 'Flashing,' he told the pilot. 'No joy yet.'

For a few long seconds he saw nothing but the luminous, flickering lines on the tubes; then, with incredible speed, a blip dropped out of the 'Christmas tree' and came racing down the trace.

'Contact at twelve thousand!' Trevarrow yelled. 'Start

turning left now, but don't throttle back. He's head-on, below and to port, and he's bloody fast!'

Kalinski whipped the Beaufighter round in a tight turn, levelling out as the other aircraft passed below them en route for London. Trevarrow was still in contact, and continued to call out the target information.

Several thousand feet ahead, Hans Lehmann gently nosed his Me 109 over into a dive. Behind the cockpit, in the space normally occupied by the radio, the X-Apparatus – an experimental, miniaturised version of the equipment used by the Heinkel pathfinders of KGr 100 – seemed to be working perfectly, picking up a clear signal from the transmitters in France and translating it into the steady tone that sounded in his headphones. The new version of X-Apparatus did not have the range of the earlier, more bulky equipment, but that did not matter; it had enough range to cover London, and the scientists who had developed it claimed that its beams were accurate and finely-tuned enough to enable a pilot to bomb a single building, provided the building was large enough and the range from the transmitters not too great.

Tonight, Hans Lehmann was out to prove the scientists' theory. His target was a gasometer at Tilbury, selected by *Luftwaffe* Intelligence because it occupied an isolated spot and it would be easy to photograph the results of the attack early the next day.

He continued his shallow dive, careful to maintain an

exact speed and course. The *Knickebein*, 'crooked leg' radio beams, as the scientists called them, had been carefully calibrated to intersect just short of the target, and the pilot had to release his 500-kg bomb at exactly the right speed and height so that it would follow a precise trajectory to the point of impact. The back-room boys had even worked out what effect the forecast winds would have on the missile's fall.

Lehmann needed all his concentration now as the speed built up, listening for the change of signal tone that would tell him when to release the bomb. It came quite suddenly, the continuous note turning into a series of morse dots. He counted them off carefully, conscious that he was holding his breath. Eighteen, nineteen, twenty . . . the twentieth note was a short dash. He pressed the bomb release, feeling the usual leap as the weapon dropped away. Then he was pulling back on the stick, sending the Messerschmitt hurtling up into the night sky, like a stone fired from a catapult.

Kalinski had been closing steadily on his target, following it down in the dive, responding to the flow of instructions from his observer. The Pole knew by now that the enemy aircraft must be a fighter-bomber; it was going much too fast to be anything else. Suddenly, Trevarrow gave an expression of surprise.

'It's broken in two! One blip is climbing fast, the other – oh, damn, I've lost it in the ground return.'

'It was a bomb,' Kalinski said grimly as he started to

pull out of the dive. 'What you saw was the Hun dropping his bomb. Now, where's the target?'

The observer peered into his visor. 'Contact lost,' he said dejectedly. 'He'll be well away by now.'

Kalinski circled. A flash he had just seen on the ground had now been replaced by a dull red glow, as whatever it was the enemy bomb had hit began to burn. Far away, on the other Channel shore, two searchlight beams suddenly came on, stabbing vertically up into the night. They looked like a pair of goalposts, and in a sense that was what they were. The ball was Lehmann's Messerschmitt, and beneath the twin beams of light was Calais-Marck airfield.

# Chapter Sixteen

Lehmann had been told to expect a briefing from somebody high up in Intelligence, but he had not expected to be confronted by a senior naval officer, a *Vizeadmiral.* It was two days since his successful trial of the blind-bombing equipment; a recce aircraft had brought back photographs of the burnt-out gasometer, so there was no doubt that the system worked, but using it needed a lot of skill, which was why Lehmann had personally selected the five most experienced pilots in the group to accompany him on the forthcoming mission. Until now, he had had no idea of what the mission was to be.

'Whitehall,' the vice-admiral said, 'and specifically this building.' He pointed to a blown-up photograph. 'This is the British Admiralty, and inside this part here is the Royal Navy's Operational Intelligence Centre. This is, without question, the nerve centre of all British naval operations across the world.'

He looked hard at the assembled group of pilots.

'I probably do not have to tell you, gentlemen, that the Führer's policy with regard to the conquest of England has changed. The invasion has been postponed until next spring, when further plans will be laid. In the meantime, everything will be done to weaken the British war effort by means of a sustained offensive against their Atlantic convoys, which are vital to the survival of the island. As you know, our U-boat fleet has already inflicted severe losses on British shipping.'

The vice-admiral paused to insert a cigarette into an ivory holder and fumbled in his tunic pockets for a lighter, looking rather annoyed when no one leaped forward to offer him a light. He found his own lighter at last and went on speaking through a cloud of aromatic smoke. Turkish, Lehmann thought absently.

'At this moment, the battleships *Admiral Scheer* and *Lutzow* are preparing to sail from Wilhemshaven. At precisely eleven o'clock tonight they will begin their passage through the North Sea; they will then sail up the coast of Norway and enter the North Atlantic via the Denmark Strait, between Iceland and Greenland. Once these fast, powerful ships are loose in the Atlantic it will be virtually impossible for the British to locate them. Every convoy on the high seas will be prey to them.'

He's getting carried away, Lehmann thought, but he

knew what the naval officer meant. The two battleships were capable of sowing terrible destruction among Britain's merchant shipping.

'The danger point,' the admiral continued, 'is when the ships are in passage through the North Sea, which is heavily patrolled by the British, and that is where you come in. We believe that a precision attack on the Admiralty building at exactly the moment when the battleships are leaving port – even though it may not result in the destruction of the Operational Intelligence Centre, which is underground and well protected – will cause such disruption to communications that no coherent orders will be issued for several hours. Even if our warships are detected, it will be some time before the British Home Fleet is able to put to sea from Scapa Flow, because of the confusion, and our ships are faster; they will not be intercepted.'

He makes it sound very simple, Lehmann mused later, after the finer details of the attack had been worked out. The experts had recalibrated the *Knickebein* transmitters so that the beams would intersect over Waterloo Station, selected as the bomb release point. Only six Me 109s were available – these were the only six that had so far been fitted with the new equipment – but their three tons of bombs, planted in a very small area, ought to do the trick.

Lehmann experienced a bout of tiredness as he waited for take-off time, and went outside for a breath of fresh air. The November night was cold, and there was an odd smell in the air. It was fog; Lehmann could scent it hours before it actually arrived. It was going to clamp down later, all right. He just hoped that Calais-Marck would stay clear of it for long enough to allow them all to get in safely after the mission. He shivered in the damp, chilly atmosphere and went back indoors, feeling no better.

The Messerschmitts took off at 22.30, with two-minute intervals between each aircraft, following their assigned courses and speeds. Lehmann, in the lead, still felt odd; it was as though a great weight were pressing down on him. He knew that something was wrong, but couldn't work out what it was. There was just an unexplained instinct that he and his pilots might be flying headlong into a trap.

To Armstrong, creeping up steadily from astern and below, Lehmann's Messerschmitt was a vague, dark outline, silhouetted against a layer of ice crystals high above. His squadron had received the order to take off only half an hour earlier, and he still felt astonishment at the precise details he had been given on the incoming raid. He had been told exactly how many enemy aircraft were involved, the tracks they would be following as they headed for the English coast, the altitude at which they would be flying. All the Beaufighter crews had to do was set up an ambush, and hope their AI equipment worked.

Kershaw had done his job, and as soon as Armstrong announced that he had visual contact with the enemy the observer had swivelled his seat round so that he could look ahead through the perspex cupola.

'It's a one-oh-nine all right,' the pilot said, 'and it's got a bloody great bomb under it. Well, here goes.'

Armstrong opened fire with the Beaufighter's cannon armament only. The noise was fearsome, the guns thudding and the aircraft shaking violently. Red flashes showed through chinks in the fuselage floor as flames came curling back from the gun ports. The air was filled with acrid smoke.

Kershaw could see that the pilot was hitting the target. White flashes sparkled on the 109's left wing, which began to stream white vapour. Bits flew off and the fighter-bomber began to roll to the right, flames streaming from it. Armstrong hastily sheered off to one side, anxious to avoid the explosion if the enemy's bomb went off.

The Messerschmitt, like a glowing comet now, went straight down and exploded somewhere north of Ashford in a vivid flash and a shower of sparks.

Armstrong could hear the excited voices of the other pilots, calling their victories over the R/T. Out over the Channel he saw streaks of fire, the burning carcases of Messerschmitts tumbling towards the sea. He still could not explain how the details of the German attack had been known with such accuracy. But then, Armstrong had never heard of Ultra, or the scientists at Bletchley Park who had broken the German naval code – the code in which the details of the night's operation had been transmitted . . .

A long time later, Hans Lehmann came to his senses

in a ploughed field. It took him a while before he remembered what had happened. Exploring himself carefully, he found a nasty gash on his head where something had ripped through his flying helmet, and his leg seemed to be broken. There was a chilling opaqueness all around him: he had been right about the fog. He wrapped himself in the silk of his parachute, and waited for daybreak.

\*

## THE END

# ENDEAVOUR INK

Endeavour Ink is an imprint of Endeavour Press.

If you enjoyed *The Intruders* check out
Endeavour Press's eBooks here:
www.endeavourpress.com

For weekly updates on our free and discounted eBooks sign up
to our newsletter:
www.endeavourpress.com

Follow us on Twitter:
@EndeavourPress

# ENDEAVOUR PRESS